THE BEST OF
CHILDREN'S
POETRY

Red Fox

A Red Fox Book
Published by Random House Children's Books
20 Vauxhall Bridge Road, London SW1V 2SA
A division of Random House UK Ltd

London Melbourne Sydney Auckland
Johannesburg and agencies throughout the world
The poems in this collection were first published in:
Cadbury's First Book of Children's Poetry
First published in 1983 by The Hamlyn Publishing Group Ltd
© Cadbury Limited 1983

Cadbury's Second Book of Children's Poetry
First published in 1984 by Beaver Books
© Cadbury Limited 1984

Cadbury's Third Book of Children's Poetry
First published in 1985 by Beaver Books
© Cadbury Limited 1985

Cadbury's Fourth Book of Children's Poetry
First published in 1986 by Beaver Books
© Cadbury Limited 1986

Cadbury's Fifth Book of Children's Poetry
First published in 1987 by Beaver Books
© Cadbury Limited 1987

Cadbury's Sixth Book of Children's Poetry
First published in 1988 by Beaver Books
© Cadbury Limited 1988

Cadbury's Seventh Book of Children's Poetry
First published in 1989 by Beaver Books
© Cadbury Limited 1989

Cadbury's Eighth Book of Children's Poetry
First published in 1990 by Red Fox
© Cadbury Limited 1990

Cadbury's Ninth Book of Children's Poetry
First published in 1991 by Red Fox
© National Exhibition of Children's Art 1991
Poems in this collection © National Exhibition of Children's Art 1992
Reprinted 1992

Set in Garamond
Typeset by JH Graphics Limited, Reading
Printed and bound in Great Britain
by Cox & Wyman Ltd, Reading, Berkshire
ISBN 0 09 918191 6

Contents

Foreword

This is a wonderful anthology and Jennifer Curry has achieved the impossible in making her selection from the nine Cadbury's Books of Children's Poetry published every year since 1983.

The poems have everything: wisdom, humour, imagination, clarity and truth and reflect the enormous enthusiasm this competition has engendered.

We are delighted therefore that from 1993, the Roald Dahl Foundation, together with Random House Children's Books and School Book Fairs, will be the new impetus behind the children's poetry competition. In September 1993, the first Roald Dahl Foundation's Poetry Competition will be launched and so the future of this great annual explosion of young creative writing is secured and in the best way possible: as a tribute to Roald Dahl, one of the greatest children's writers of our time.

In this book we can both celebrate the best of the Cadbury era and savour the prospect of an exciting new beginning for this important poetry competition.

Richard Morris-Adams
Chairman
The National Exhibition of Children's Art

The National Exhibition
of Children's Art

Preface

by Jennifer Curry, series editor

My first memory of NECA's Poetry Competition goes back to a morning in 1983 when I sat at my table dazzled both by the early spring sunshine and by the poems selected for Book 1. I hadn't realized till then that children could write with such perception, clarity, wit and compassion. From drugs to daffodils, computers to child abuse, nothing seemed beyond their poetic grasp.

Over the 8 years that followed, my delight in the poetry and the children's exuberant response to life never diminished. Some especially talented individuals emerged as year after year their work fought its way through from the many thousands of poems that were submitted to achieve publication and sometimes prizes. Though the poems we judged were always anonymous, we often re-discovered the same writers several years running. 14-year-old Emma Payne appeared in '83, then in '84, before winning an Italian Tour Award in '85. Catherine Wilkinson first arrived as a 13-year-old in '88, and in '91 carried off the Individual Gold Medal Award. Many others, like Arnold Hunt and Tony Roberts, proved their talent by consistently getting into print. Nicholas Perks enchanted the judges with his lyrical 'Day of the Daffodils' in '86, then astonished us by re-emerging after 5 years with a satirical attack on the House of Commons. But perhaps the highest accolade must go to Rosemary Cowan, whose work we published only once, in '85. Her poetic response to her native Northern Ireland, and to the death of her father, expressed a taut, disciplined anguish which moved us profoundly and won her an Italian Tour Award.

As with individual writers, so with schools. Many sent us folios of excellent work but the material produced by Debenham High School, James Allen's Girls' School and King's School Canterbury was consistently outstanding. Every year we were impressed not only by the high standard of the writing but also of the teaching that lay behind it.

During the 9 years of the competition the quality of the children's work remained constant but some aspects of their subject matter changed. They always enjoyed writing about themselves, school, their families, their pets. Every year they were concerned about social issues – loneliness, poverty, old age, war, starvation, racism, discrimination, cruelty. Disasters changed, famine in Ethiopia one year, a terrorist attack another, but their compassionate response never wavered. They always wrote with joy about the natural world, and with anxiety about pollution and environmental threats, but that anxiety grew more acute as the years progressed. Sometimes the contents of the book have shown an odd an unaccountable 'blip'. In 1985 we were treated to a positive feast of exquisite love poems, many of them by boys.

With all these riches to choose from it has been difficult to select the best of the best. My choice has had to be a personal one, and perhaps idiosyncratic, but I worked to specific criteria. I looked for;
★ a genuine child's eye view of the world,
★ originality of thought, content and treatment,
★ freshness of language and imagery,
★ competent use of form, structure and the meaning of words,
★ humour, wit, commitment, and a clarity of comment.
  I also wanted the complete book:
★ to reflect the whole of childhood experience: good, bad, painful, funny, sad, boring . . .
★ to give a fair representation of the complete body of work that has been published since 1983, and

★ to stand up in its own right as a cohesive, well-balanced, representative anthology of children's poetry.

I hope that every reader will enjoy sharing in this special world of childhood as much as I have done.

Juniper Curran

In the Beginning . . .

Enter: a child

That's your cue. Break a leg!
Play your part well.
Brighten up this stage of darkness;
Go and join the jesters' scene.
The audience will be your judge;
Be laughed at and mocked
But don't forget your lines.
There is no prompt,
You have had no rehearsal
And the script has not been completed.
Break a leg!

Jane Bishop (14)
Debenham High School,
Stowmarket, Suffolk
(Cadbury's Gold Award for Schools)
1991

I See, I Feel

The journey

It's dark in here – it's warm and safe.
My very own space – for me to grow.
Inside this bubble, far away – yet very near.

I can hear the unceasing beat – beating for me –
    A rhythm soft and sweet.
I cannot see, or smell or taste . . .
But I can touch within my place.

My place is changing . . .
I'm squeezed and pushed –
What's happening now?
Confusion . . . fear,
My place is left behind.

This is a dreadful thing,
I'm pushing downwards,
The rhythm has all gone.
Where am I now?

The pushing stops . . .
I'm somewhere else!
This somewhere does not push me now.
I'm feeling free – yet still afraid.
My eyes are opening,
I see, I feel, new things are here.
A soft sensation, like my special place.

A gentle touch, a murmur soft and sweet.
Loving hands – these are my friends.
I am born –
I am loved –
I am me.

Caroline Scott (9)
Healey County Primary School,
Rochdale, Lancashire
1990

On my very first day at school

I got up in the morning
And s   t   r   e   t   c   h   e   d.
I padded to the bathroom
And reached,
H
I
G
H
For my toothbrush.
My clothes hung high in the cupboard.
I stood on my tip-toes
I tried to make myself a giant
To reach them.
I felt as though I was growing,

'It's time to go,' Mum said.
It seemed miles
Oh, what a way to go,
A million, trillion miles.
I said, 'Don't leave me!'
Too late.
She – – – – – – – – – – – – was gone,
I reached H for my peg
        I
        G
        H BIGGEST and
I knew only the
Strongest giant could reach it.
Oh, how heavy my coat was.

I walked into the class room.
I was shivering.
She gave us some work.
I need a pencil.
I took one from the teacher's desk.
The teacher said 'Where has my pencil gone?'
I asked if I could go and throw something away.
I took the pencil and threw it away
And hoped it would turn up another day.

The bell rang RING RING!!

I jumped out of my skin
My mum was waiting outside.
She said, 'Well, what was it like?'
I said, 'I can't wait till tomorrow!'

Lucy Crisp (12)
St Gregory's Comprehensive School,
Bath, Avon
1991

'First Day at School'
Rachel Hodgkinson (9)
1986

Excited

I
 s
  l
   i
    d
     e
     d
      o
       w
        n
         t
          h
           e
            b
             a
              n
               i
                s
                 t
                  e
                   r
                    s

                    can't wait!

I do not $have$ breakfast because $I'm$ too
E X C I T E D
My arms S_HA^KE and $S^H_A{}_KE$ and S_HA^KE
My tummy $T^IC^KL_ES$ and $T^IC^KL_ES$

O P E N I T !

Mark Powell (7)
Nunnery Wood Primary School,
Worcester
1989

My fight

It all started by my friend
pinching me.
I pinched him back,
and then we started to fight.
We started kicking and punching,
Biff Baff oooch,
ooo that hurt, kick.
I put my fist up
I punched him.
Everybody shouts and screams,
Everybody is joining in.
Everybody is kicking and thumping,
they all shout oooch ooo.
Then my Mummy comes outside,
She sees it and stops it.
So we have to stop it and make friends again.

Jamie Vacca (7)
Thorpe Junior School, Peterborough, Cambs
1985

I was crying

I was crying
I could not draw a circle.
I was crying
Because I could not understand.
I used compasses.
Other people knew,
But I couldn't get them to work.
I do not ask the right questions.
Who can I ask?
My parents and my teacher.
I ask them and they explain.
I still cannot draw a circle
I cried,
I could not understand,
but I tried.

Laura Potts (8)
Benton Park Primary School,
Newcastle-upon-Tyne
1991

When I am angry

When I get angry I start
    screaming
and screeching
    raging
and hating
    smashing
and biting
    crying
and punching
    leaving
and breaking
    throwing
and destroying
    steamed up
and blowing up
    slam doors
and stamping
    exploding
and strangling
    cuddling
and kissing
    sorrys
and quiet again.

Ian White (8)
Buxlow Prep School,
Wembley, Middx
1986

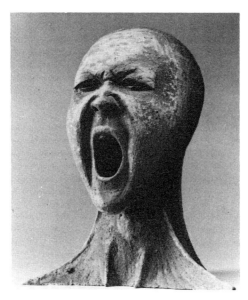

'The Scream'
Scott Shepherd (17)
Buckhaven High School,
Buckhaven, Fife
(Highly commended)
1989

On me . . . as a dustbin

Sometimes I feel like a dustbin
Filled and ever filling
With things disposable
Junk food
Polluted air
Adults' opinions.
And I say
'STOP, STOP
You're filling me
Too full!'
And they say
'TOUGH'
And teach me
TRIGONOMETRY.

I want to know what happens
When I flip my lid.

?

Helen Goff (15)
Uxbridge, Middlesex
1989

What's that down there?

What's that down there?
What's that moving?
What's that moving down
in the dark?
Is it the monster
Who roars
And kills?
Or is it the skeleton
Who rattles his bones?
What's that down there?
What's that moving?
What's that moving down
in the dark?
Is it a bat
Flying through the air?
What's that
in the dark?

Jonathan Matthews (7)
St George's County Junior
School, Copthorne,
Shrewsbury
1989

Fishing

The float goes under
my eyes pop out
my mind is in a whirl
as I reel it in
and in
and in
and in
and in
and in
and in

this big.

Richard Hemstock (10)
South Green Junior
School,
Billericay, Essex
1990

'*A Boat Trip*'
Laura Chesman (7)
Hill West First School,
Sutton Coldfield, W. Midlands
1991

The storm that night

Then the flat water rippled, slapped into billows,
And came tumbling and chasing amongst the crests
    and the hollows.
Waves curled, spun into foam as they fought and
    followed;
Then black sudden dark. The storm-giants heaved
    and wallowed –
Roaring, they trod water and joyously bellowed.

But next day, fishing in smooth water for flickering
    minnows,
We splashed shoreward in sand and caressing
    shallows.

Arnold Hunt (15)
Hendon, London
(Highly commended)
1985

On my bike

Two turns on the pedals and
I'm off on my own,
Getting faster and faster,
Speeding down a hill at a
thousand miles per hour,
The world whizzing past me in
a flash.
The wind in my face stinging
me like lots of little needles.
My hands feel numb against
the handlebars.
I feel freezing on the outside
but hot and sweaty on the
inside.
I feel tension building up inside
me as I jump over a bump and
cling on to the handlebars for
dear life.
I come to a rough surface,
the ground is spitting stones
at me as my wheels crunch
through the gravel.
I screech on my back brake,
skid around and brace myself
to go up again.

Thomas Hollett (11)
RA Butler Junior School,
Saffron Walden, Essex
1990

I can't take the sun

I can't take the sun no more, Man.
I buy fifty cans of cola,
I take my clothes off,
But I'm still hot.
I might as well take off my skin
It's so so so so hot, Man.
I just can't take the sun no more.
I might as well take myself apart
Before the sun melts me.
It's so so so so so so so so so
Hot, Man.
Just can't take the sun, Man.

Linval Quinland (10)
Grasmere Primary School,
Stoke Newington, London
1990

Rock music

Tension is building,
Can you feel it?
You can never be prepared,
No matter how you try.
The guitar howls and screams,
And a drummer fights his kit.
The volume builds up,
And it flows to a crescendo.
You can feel the energy from beneath,
Bursting from the ground, and spiralling up your legs.
It makes you want to run,
It makes you want to shout,
It makes you want to tear down the walls that stop you
    getting out.

Marcus Knight (14)
Wymondham High School,
Wymondham, Norfolk
1989

'New Wave Group'
Merrywood Boys School
(Highly commended)
1987

Christmas joy

The audience, chilled from the frosty night
Fumbled into the stuffy hall.
Silver stars clung,
Tinsel was drooped around the crammed room.
They sat, not knowing what to expect
From a group of children wearing old curtains
And tinsel round their heads.
The hall grew warmer,
A light beamed on to a home-made crib.
A cloth was draped over Jesus' worn face.
Backstage everyone was excited,
Except me.
Hot and clammy, I sat in a corner
Waiting for my turn.
I was pushed on to the stage
And blinded.
My angel's costume was crumpled,
My face was numb.
I could see the Headmaster
Lounging in his plastic chair.
He gave a smile,
Urging me to speak.
One eye gave a friendly wink.
It was Christmas.

Helen Robinson (13)
Brandeston Hall School,
Brandeston, Suffolk
1990

First day of the holidays

It's early.

My body is heavy and relaxed.
My tousled head, warm in the hollow of the pillow.
My eyes feel delightfully fresh and cool.

It's excitement.

A bubbling underground spring,
longing to burst free,
to express effervescently the undiscovered.

It's ecstasy.

Like the birth of a sneeze.
The sparkling crest of a yawn.
The calm, after spasms
of perpetual hiccups.

I stretch.
And throw wide my sunfilled curtains
of happiness.

Nikki Field (13)
Tunbridge Wells, Kent
1985

Theatre

I saw a play the critics called touching
It did not touch me
It leapt into my soul and
ripped out every secret I had
It paraded them up and down the aisles
All my black things with banners on
stood onstage and
pointed me out to the world
In my seat I wanted to scream
and jump on to the stage
to wrench my life back from the players.

Imane Massoud (15)
International School of London, London
(Highly commended)
1988

Unstoppable Yellow

The day of the daffodils

In some quiet corner of some quiet garden,
The first one appears
A drop of colour in a drab world.

Soon there comes another, and another,
A blaze of colour
Bursting and growing unstoppable yellow.

This is only the start of the attack
The advance forces
Struggling to survive in a cruel world.

It is a highly organized advance,
Like a military campaign,
A war against colourlessness.

Nicholas Perks (11)
Dalkeith, Scotland
(Highly commended)
1986

Spring

When I see the yellow aconites,
Hear the thrushes sing,
Touch the furry catkins,
I know it must be spring.

Kate Moss (10)
Hexham, Northumberland
1989

Sweet dream

Pushing the sun along in my pushchair,
She giggled,
So did I,
And woke myself up.

Adele Inugai-Dixon (4)
Stoke Park, Ipswich
(Highly commended)
1988

Summer

The heat-haze hovers, humming
Over the bleached grass,
Crickets chirp busily among the grains.
A step is heard from far away,
Sandals slapping the age-worn stones,
Creating miniature dust-storms beside the bustling
    ants.
A lizard lazily lolls on
A scorched brown stone –
His eyes blink, and tongue flicks.
A plum drops, dark and ripe,
Followed by a broken leaf.

A dry straw hat lies
Carelessly upon the path –
A tired yellow ribbon flaps,
Fanned by a gentle breeze,
And the dry grass bends seriously to work.
The crickets rustle and sing, unseen,
While the world revolves.

Charlotte Davies (15)
Convent of Our Lady of Providence,
Alton, Hants
1987

Salty sea

Salty sandcastle,
Salty sea,
Salty footprints,
Salty me.

Carl Saville (5)
Beehive Lane
Primary School,
Chelmsford, Essex
1991

'On the Beach'
Richard Juby (11)
1984

Rockets

A match alight
A rocket racing into the air
And coming down in
rainbows of rage

Jonathan Brown (7)
St Erth County Primary
School,
Hayle, Cornwall
1990

My Christmas thought

Robin Redbreast
On a silver tree,
Glowing in the moonlight.

Cherry Hiscox (6)
Gaer Infant School,
Newport, Gwent
1988

Winter

It is cold today,
On the window this morning is a pattern.
There's a puddle of glass in the street.
Your cheeks are red and glowing as if they are on
    fire.
I shall warm my hands on your red cheeks.

Ernest Ogbonnaya (7)
Turnham Junior School,
Brockley, London
(Highly commended)
1987

Pigs

Pigs are big and pink and round,
They sniff along the muddy ground,
And when they see a nice soft spot,
They jump in with a happy plop.

Katie Sandford (9)
1984

My teacher

My teacher is like a bouncy bed
Comfortable and safe but fun
Like sunrise, calm but welcome and
bright
She's a strawberry, juicy and sweet
A warm and sunny summer day
A squirrel busily scuttling around.

Rebecca Mansell and Natasha May (9)
Pentlepoir County Primary School,
Saundersfoot, Dyfed
1991

Mrs Power played the tambourine

Twisting, diving,
Then a swoop.
Banging, clanging,
Loop the loop.
Ribbons tossing,
Clash and smash.

Swirl or twirl,
Dart or curl.
A flick of the wrist.
A sharp little kick.
Sometimes slow
And sometimes quick.

Robin L. Gillyon (8)
Bedgrove County
First School,
Aylesbury, Bucks.
1986

ssshhh! Listen!

This bass has been walking all night,
Swinging to the rhythm,
Simply, singing.
Not off beat,
no repetition
Swaying, someone's listening.
No ending
it's still projecting
thoughts, feelings
never ending.
Brushing drums,
synchronized swirls,
comfortable as it always is as
each . . . brush . . . falls.
The piano trips over several staggering solo
semibreves,
Silence.
A subtle opening phrase.
The muted trumpet tells you,
'I guess I'll have to change my plan'
overlapping a singing note,
saxophone cuts in,
Plays a run,
plays this run again,
offering you a warm glow
that controls how you think.

You smile and close your eyes,
let me hear it one more time!

Joe Broughton (13)
Chester,
Cheshire
1991

'Harmonica Player'
Michael Salvage (17)
1986

Origami

We were snaking along the road.
Everyone was rattling.
The teacher hissed 'Be quiet or we're never
going to get there.'
(We were going to our local library
to see a demonstration.)
'Do any of you know what origami is?'
'Yes Miss. It's self defence.'
'No! Do you, Alec?'
'Origami. The art of paper folding.
It originated in Japan.'
'Smart Alec!
Here we are. The library and our origami demonstration.
You may sit. Fold your arms.'
Funny. I thought it was paper
we were meant to be folding!
The man giving the demonstration had fingers
as agile as an acrobat
as he twisted and turned the paper.
The folds in the paper matched my brows!
Well, as you can imagine
when we had a go we were in a flap . . .
never mind the bird.
Then it was all over.
We headed back to school.
Inspired we were.
Trouble was, by the time we got back
we'd forgotten most of it.
The birds had flown!

Emma Cooper (11)
Cloudside County Junior School,
Sandiacre, Nottingham
1989

S-t-r-e-t-c-h-i-n-g

Waking up
in the morning
is lovely,
Especially when you s-t-r-e-t-c-h.
You open up
your legs and arms
and stretch.
It's just lovely.
The feeling just makes
you want to do it
over and over again.
But after a while
your stretch
runs out
and it's over.

Sharon Cheeks (10)
1984

I love my belt

Plastic belt
Elastic belt
Stretch – stretch – stretch
FANTASTIC belt.

Jasmine Lehal (5)
Bedford, Bedfordshire
1991

Mummie's skirt

Pick me up in your wonderful skirt,
all the day long!

Anna Burgess (4)
Bewbush Home School,
Crawley, Sussex
(Silver Medal Award Winner)
1991

Down in the Dumps

A visit to the doctor

I went to the doctor's
And guess what I had!

I had spots on my bots,
And splinters in my knickers,
And I hid in the loo
Because I had the flu,
And tonsillitis
And fleabiters.
I was down in the dumps
Because I had mumps
And bumps
And lumps,
And even my toy beaver
Had a dose of the fever.

The doctor said, 'Try these!
Here's pink pills and green pills and blue pills
And horrible medicine.'
Ugh!

Robin Gillyon (7)
Bedgrove County First School,
Aylesbury, Bucks
(Highly commended)
1985

Mumps

I'm down in the dumps,
Because I've got mumps!
I hope it goes soon—
It's like a balloon!
It hurts when I yawn
And it hurts when I chew,
And sometimes I wish
That they'd change me for new!

Now DON'T call me fussy,
Because I am NOT!
I have to take tablets
And they make me hot!
I can't move around –
(That's unusual for me!)
I can't eat my breakfast,
My dinner . . . OR . . . tea!

I can't go to school
'cos my cheeks are so fat;
I look like a hamster –
I giggle at THAT!
I pull funny faces –
It helps pass the time;
I laid down and thought . . .
Then I made up this rhyme!

Nicola Jane Field (9)
1983

'My Brother'
Iain Sturrock (14)
1984

My teeth

I am losing my teeth
I have lost two
If I lose any more
I won't be able to chew.

Jennifer Godfrey (5)
Crofty, Swansea,
W. Glamorgan
1985

I hurt myself

Blood running
Cut my finger bad
Brick
      Tripped
            Oops
Squished in the mud
Wet
Called
      Dale
Rain falling.

Tony Sulieman (7)
Denaby Main Infant
School,
Doncaster,
South Yorkshire
1990

I've got a lithp

Thome one pleathe help me,
I find it hard to thpeak.
My lithp ith tho incredible,
It getth worth every week.

Having a lithp ith no fun,
It can be embarathing.
It'th bad when you're talking,
But worth when you thing.

People thtop and lithten,
Thometimeth they even laugh.
When I'm being therioth,
They think I've made a gaff.

Thopping ith a problem,
When everybody thtareth.
The thop athithtanth look at me,
And thome don't theem to care.

They jutht thit and thtare at me,
Ath if I wath a rock.
Thometimeth they don't therve me,
Until I give them a thock.

Speaking rather upperclass,
Makes them think again.
They serve me straight away,
Is it some sort of game?

My lisp is now completely gone,
Many say that it's a boon.
But there are times I miss it,
And hope it comes back thoon.

Keith Howard (15)
Cramlington, Northumberland
1990

Me

I worry a lot
Boy do I worry
On Mondays I worry
On Tuesdays I worry
On Every day of the week
I worry
I worry about anything
and everything.

I'd like to be someone
who doesn't worry
Boy do I wish I didn't
worry
Here I go again worrying
about worrying
I wish I didn't worry about
worrying about worrying.

James Cann (11)
1983

Thumbs down

A year ago I mislaid my thumbs,
You know the fingers that aren't.
I pulled my hand from beneath the bed
and found five and six had departed.
Those irresponsible digits had gone and
left me disabled.
Without them how could I hitch a lift
Or pick up a pencil to draw?
Thumbs down to them, I say.

Mark Bell (10)
St Wilfred's School
Haywards Heath, Sussex
1986

The brine

The place for me,
Is not the sea.
Not when I think,
That I might sink.
Another thing,
Jellyfish sting.
And crabs have claws.
And sharks have jaws.
Out in the sun,
The waves look fun.
But underneath,
Are horrid teeth!

Fred Woods (11)
1984

Visitors

People are coming to stay.
You can tell.
Mum's putting the toys back in their box,
moving the dolls' cot by the window.

I hate it when visitors come.

She's checking the dinner, chicken and trifle;
she's putting her new dress on;
the doorbell rings.

Any second now I'll hear

Hello, darling!
My! How you've grown.

Rachel Hodges (11)
Tupton Hall School,
Chesterfield, Derbys
1988

The spider

First he's in the bathroom,
Then he's in the hall,
Then he's in the kitchen –
I can't stand it at all.
Then he's in my bedroom,
I nearly had a fright.
And then he crawled all over me
In the middle of the night!

Penny Armstrong (7)
London
1986

'A Bedspread for
Granny'
Sarah Johnson (17)
Franklin
Sixth Form College
Grimsby
S. Humberside
1991

Aristotle and Ballcocks

They sent me to see the careers man,
He was in a posh office down town,
I tried to be pleasant and friendly,
But all I received was a frown.

'I'm sorry to have to inform you,
But it takes more than three CSEs,
Especially as one is in woodwork,
And the others are only grade threes,

'It takes years of hard work to be one,
Philosophers aren't trained they are born,
And besides your "qualifications",
There isn't a box on the form.'

So he sent me away with a leaflet,
To get on a GYOS*
By the time I walked home from the bus stop,
I thought, 'O hell, what a mess!'

When I told my dad, he couldn't stop laughing,
His face went all purple and red,
And when he recovered from choking,
He told me, 'Try plumbing instead,'

So I looked it up on my leaflet,
And filled in the space on the form,
I read up on ballcocks and U-bends,
And reflected the fate of a pawn.

If Descartes had had this problem,
And Aristotle and Socrates too,
We might not have had great thinkers,
But just think of the showers and loos!

So I went back to see the careers man,
Who said, 'It's a safer idea,
To stick to something more normal,
A job and not a career.'

Emma Payne (14)
(Highly commended)
1983

**Government Youth Opportunity Scheme as
it was called when I wrote this.*

Noises

Bang Bang
Clang Clang
Clink Clink
Chink Chink
Washing machine's on the blink!

Karen Parker (9)
Boulton Junior School,
Alvaston, Derbyshire
1985

Haiku

Haiku is not fun;
I really do not like it,
But I can write it.

Daniel Einon (13)
Fortismere School,
Tetherdown,
London
1985

Royal haiku

They all say 'God save
The Queen': I don't know what
To save the Queen from.

Daniel Burwood (12)
Swanbourne House School,
Milton Keynes, Buckinghamshire
1991

'The Queen Visiting
the
Royal Norfolk Show'
Rachel Groom (7)
1987

Poem of protest

Poem of Protest, he told us to write.

Poem of Protest indeed.

Why I could protest on lots of things
Like going to bed,
Or nettle stings,

But I think I'll protest on writing a
Poem of Protest, that protests about things.

Katie Joanne Burrows (11)
1984

I Know What I'll Play

Toes

I just *can't* get to sleep,
But I know what I'll play,
Every night it's the same
To my mother's dismay.

I'll pull back the bedclothes
And slide out my feet –
'Ten toes are now starring
in "Nutcracker Suite"!'

There's a mark on the big one,
It's been there a year,
Since 'what Aunt Maud did'
When she berthed in her chair!

The spotlights are on them
(This flexilamp's brill!)
I'll tear up some tissues
For skirts with a frill.

My nails are like birds' claws!
It's the latest 'in' look!
If you pull your toes up –
There's a stand for your book.

'Enter – Sugar Plum Fairy'
(Keep the rest in the wings –
tucked under the bedclothes.)
The telephone rings.

Mum creeps up the stairs
But the fun hasn't ended –
She played that in school
And was nearly suspended!

Nicola Jane Field (10)
1984

Blocks

When I build a tower a house or a town
they always say lovely
now please take it down
and put all your blocks very neatly away
I wish for once they
would let them stay

Susan Guest (8)
1983

China dolls

Lifeless pale-faced dolls,
Colour faded with age.
Sun-drained Victorian clothes
Glassy eyes, some long lost
The dolls that stare are the dolls that scare.
They sit on dusty shelves,
Caged in with glass,
Cherry-red rose-bud lips
Innocent exhibits in museums and
Stately homes.
I see them come to life
Sinister horrors that haunt my dreams.

Keir Taylor (12)
Argoed High School,
Mold, Clwyd
1987

'Untitled'
Tracy Wary (15)
1985

My box model

Now what I did is . . .
I didn't know that I could
Make this do something.
This flapping bit . . .
I didn't know that I could use
All this sticky stuff.
That flicks into here
And then it goes down into a bucket.
I pretend somebody's being poorly
And the model is a nurse's machine
I didn't know I could do this.
I bet my mum will love it.

Paul Morris (5)
Havannah County Primary School,
Congleton, Cheshire
1991

Maybe outside

Go and open the door.
Maybe outside there's a dish
And on that dish is a silver fish
With waving fins in a golden light.

Go and open the door.
Maybe outside there's a princess
Wearing a beautiful dress
Singing a song about herself.

Go and open the door.
Maybe outside there's a magic toy box
With a dancing doll and talking sailors,
And an elephant which plays with you all the time.

Go and open the door.
Maybe outside there's a swimming pool
With lots of laughing children in it.
Diving and swimming and playing.
Perhaps they'll let you join the fun.

Cathy Vincent (8)
Sandy Hill School,
St Austell, Cornwall
1985

Skating

When I try to skate
My feet are so wary
They grit and grate;
And then I watch Mary
Easily gliding
Like an icy-fairy;
Skimming and curving
Out and in,
With a turn of her head,
And lift of her chin,
And a gleam of her eye,
And a twirl and a spin;
Sailing under
The breathless hush
Of the willows and back
Of the frozen rush;
Out of the island

And round the edge,
Swerving close
To the popular route,
And round the lake
On a single foot,
With a two, and a three
And a loop, and a ring;
Where Mary glides
The lake will sing!
Out in the mist
I hear her now
Under the frost,
Of the willow-bough
Easily sailing,
Light and fleet
With a song of the lake
Beneath her feet.

Carol Kemp (13) and Nicola McMaster (13)
Sheraton Comprehensive School,
Stockton-on-Tees,
Cleveland
1985

Seven snowmen

We built seven
Snowmen my
brother and me.
Some of them
had no heads.
Some of them
were fat. Some
of them had
faces, and
some didn't.
All of them
Were different,
But one thing
They were all
Cold. And so
Were we!
My brother
and me.

Vanessa Steele (5)
White Hills
Lower School,
Northampton
(Highly
commended)
1989

Old man wind

Old Man Wind,
Why do you blow the trees to make them shiver?
Why do you whistle in the small gaps?
Why do you roar like a hundred dragons?
Why do you chase the gentle leaves?
Why do you push the small green grass?
Why do you pull my hair?
Go away
Until I want you
To fly my kite.

Mark Gardner (7)
Bedgrove County First School,
Aylesbury, Bucks
1987

'Beech Wood'
Victor Lewis (14)
1983

The tree climb

The sun shining in my eyes,
I scrabble around the tree,
Looking for a branch stump.
I look up and see a branch,
Just out of reach.
I jump up and grab it.
It is wet and slimy.
My hands slip!
Wildly I grab,
But fall,
To land on my feet.
I look at my hands;
They are wet and slightly grazed.
The smell of wet bark and moss.
Again I try:
This time I get more grip.
I dangle like a helpless spider,
My feet walking up the tree until
They reach the branch.
I sit there for a while
And smell
The wet bark,
And hear
The leaves rustling like milk bottle tops.

And the sun is shining in my eyes.

Peter Watts (11)
Halesworth Middle School,
Halesworth, Suffolk
1985

73

The alley behind the chemist's

There's an alley where me and my mates go
Behind the chemist's at Carner Street
It's nothing special just a few old dustbins
and empty wooden crates, but it's
our alley, our private place where we can
play cars or tag
If you come near it Big Midge will
get you

It's much better than home
there's no privacy at home just disturbance
only me and my mates know
where it is
don't tell anyone

Hannah Ford (11)
Bishop of Llandaff Church in Wales School,
Llandaff, Mid Glamorgan
1990

Owed to a fruit machine

One more coin
won't hurt
One more coin
could be the difference
between starvation and tomorrow
One more coin
and nothing else
for today.

Through the slot
of a metal machine
Through the slot
and into oblivion
deciding whether I win or lose
Through the slot
and nothing else
for today.

Turning reels
that spin
Turning reels
that have the power
to answer all my prayers tonight
Turning reels
and nothing else
for today.

Lemon, cherry, bar
no win
Lemon, cherry, bar
has destroyed my dreams
but rekindled the craving
Lemon, cherry, bar
and nothing else
for today.

One more coin
won't hurt
One more coin . . .

And nothing else . . .

Catherine Wilkinson (13)
Buckden, Huntingdon, Cambs
1988

The cavemen

Under the stage, in an alley of mattresses and paper, we
    dwelt:
Timmy, Johnnie and I. It was dark there:
Blackboard black, black ink black, and scholar's gown
    black.
But did we take a torch? Only when we looked at
        Timmy's naughty magazines.
We were too virile to take a torch.
Only scaredy-cats took a torch.

Breaks and lunchtimes were the best times. Having our
    biscuits
There and talking about morning lessons was strangely
        enjoyable.
Sometimes people rehearsed plays when we were down in the
    'caves'.
Suddenly, I would say, 'KV', and we would lie still under
        the mattresses, not breathing if we could manage it.
We were rarely caught.

When we were nine and too old to use the I-didn't-
      know-the-rules excuse,
We went there and discovered the airing system.
Timmy's Swiss army knife loosened the gauze and we
    were in.
We kept crawling like James Bond and Steve McQueen
      in *The Great Escape.*
It was like a cave – pitch black. I led the way, my jelly
Hands in front to see if there was a wall to bump into.
The first time we stayed on the main path,
But other times we did not.

Finally, one misty, cold, boring day, when we were ten,
We went down the 'cave' and found Billy Thomson's and
      Jason Bell's signatures all over the wall.
Someone else had entered our secret place.
There was no point in going there now.
We were no longer cavemen. We were homeless.

Michael Davies (14)
The King's School,
Canterbury, Kent
(Silver Medal and Most Promising Individual Award Winner)
1991

Attacking missile base three

I ran across the long playground.
I jumped behind some stumpy logs.
ZAP! ZAP!
My lazer-blaster fired.
I ran past the crystallized being.
'Missile Bases One and Two destroyed,' my CB
   crackled.
Twzap! ZAP!
I jumped over the ruins of Missile Base Two.
A loud explosion,
A big bang,
A shower of sparks.
I threw myself down.
BANG!!!
POW!
PLANG!
KOWPANG!
BANG!!
I was engulfed in flames.
I got up,
Brushed the bits of iron off myself,
'Mission completed,' I said.
Life-support-suit burnt,
I walked through the smoke,
Then had a rest.
Dead silence.
Missile Base Three blasterized.
'Three down and one to go,' cackled Ben on the
   radio,
ZAP!
Another bogeyman I thought.

ZAP!
ZAP!
POW!
ZAP!
POW!
POW!
ZAP!
ARRRGGHH!!
Silence.
From the flames I approached it . . .
I threw down the pin,
I threw the rugger ball,
ORRING! the bell went.
I went into missile base
ULTIMATE.

James Parsons (9)
Dulwich College Preparatory School,
Cranbrook, Kent
1987

'Starting'
Catherine Jenkins
(15)
Croesyceiliog
Comprehensive
School,
Cwmbran, Gwent
1991

Childflit

When he tiptoed alone
Through sunlit lanes
And sung swayed
Child-flit games
In the shadow parabled barns
He daydreamt.

And even though the church sermons
Beckoned him in,
He turned away
To song to the streams
Where the ring of hushed benedictions
Slowly swayed.

O, childflood lullayed days,
The linked hours in love with the horses
Sky-dome-chimes
Through heavens behind clouds through his fingers
On the high hammocked hangar
In the mid-day aisles of sun.

So giddied by the gadding swing
He dives to the hay,
At love with life
And play and see
The rust of sky-flight filter with the breeze.

Time passes – fly the busy wrens
Ducking and diving through the dappled drones
   from the sky,
In love with the foxes
And still shy in front
Of the goats' tails and tongues
In the vein of summer
Runround like dragonfly – wings on the pond.

And the ganders
Gone from their pens –
long ago gone.
Then he climbs and falls
Gashed and rung, swung
And giddied by summer's swing
Sepulchral-shadowed sound
Echoing over the hanging hills . . .
Crepuscule.

And the swaying clocks free from time
Chime . . . incessantly
And autumn dives its leaves
And grieves summer's fainting sky
Time and time, time goes on.

And the lovers of the lakes entwined – and be gay
And linked hours
Mingled mimes
Make time play stay
Yet the clock still chimes
Their rhymes fold time.

Jesse Witcombe (14)
London
(Award winner)
1987

'Duck Taking Off'
Matthew Manley (6)
St Augustine of
Canterbury School,
Dowend, Bristol
1991

Remembrance

Scrambling through the undergrowth,
Gasping for breath, heart pumping wildly,
Pushing the tall creepers to one side.
A burst of gunfire to the left,
Thudding of a body falling to the ground,
Movement in front, running away.
Sweat pouring down a hot face,
The grinding of teeth and a rip of cloth,
A movement to the right.
Over there!
Muscles bulging, tense:
Lifting a rifle
A shot echoing through the silence,
A piercing scream
The Enemy falls dead,
Blood trickling from his brow
Mixing with perspiration . . .

The old one-legged man
Sat on the park bench
Watching the small boys with sticks
Running down the path.
'Bang! Bang! you're dead!'
A make-believe scream,
The Enemy fell down,
And as he watched, he remembered.

Alistair McLeish (12)
1984

I Kept Looking

Feet

Her hairy feet
Were in horny sandals,
She had a flowing dress
And a nosy smile.
Funny, toes with square ends.
When she was talking
She pressed her face close,
Till I could see each
Coarse grey hair
On her chin.
Her toenails were yellow.
She shut one eye
And stroked a hand
Down a prickly leg,
Where great veins fed
A fat mole in the hollow of her ankle.

I tried to answer her questions
But I kept looking at her feet.

Katie-Louise Thomas (16)
Chelsfield, Kent
(Italian Tour Award winner)
1989

She called it her robin

She called it her robin.
And once she took me to see.
All she did
Was outstretch her hand
And sprinkle
Cheese crumbs
On the palm.
She would call softly,
'Robby, Robby.'
Nothing happened at first,
But then,
A rose bush
Sprang to life
As her robin,
Wings vibrating,
Flew from his nest in the roots.

He landed, delicately,
On her palm.
His breast was brick red,
The edges a musty orange
Fading into the brown of his back.
His eyes shone,
Chips of wet flints
Smoothed round.
His beak was like the tip
Of a rose thorn
As he pecked for the cheese.

She spoke to him soothingly,
Dragging out the vowel sounds,
'Robby, my little Robby,'
The tip of her little finger
Tracing down his back
As she lovingly stroked
Her fickle friend.

Lara Mair (12)
Halesworth Middle School,
Halesworth, Suffolk
(Arthur Lines Poetry Award winner)
1988

Could you pass me the salt, please?

I saw a man on a bike,
                panting.
He had no fingers
and only one thumb.

I looked at the trees.
How could he ride?
I don't know,
I didn't want to stare.

Later,
painfully,
he passed me the salt.
I just smiled.

Rachel Cooke (16)
Sheffield, S. Yorks
1987

Pointing

The woman is thin
Pointing to what could be
Anything, up in the sky
Pointing with all her body
Her feet
Her waist
Her hair
All the way up to her finger
Large and motionless.

What is she pointing at
Nobody knows
Her expression shows
Want and need facing upwards.
Her dress long and thin
Her hair hanging, poised
Waiting for something to happen.
Something terrible?
Something wonderful?
Something historic?
Something special?

Her hands were
Big and lumpy,
One pointing
One clutching her heart.

Sophie Rickard (9)
Whalley CE Primary School,
Whalley, Blackburn, Lancs
1989

Bowling green

Hedged round with privet
As with habit and with age,
Move the bowlers
On the lawn that is their stage.

Their gestures inflame the air
Like impatient clouds
Gathering to some point far away
That the sunset shrouds

And weighs with red.
The arm swings forward while the eye
Is calm that contemplates the speed.
Marvellous, the silent rounded cry

Of motion, ending
In collision.
Then come measuring-tapes,
Disagreement and confusion.

Is this Olympus where the Gods
Spin the dark planets, holding fate
In hands tobacco-stained?
Or can they only hope the bowl runs straight?

Lucy Barker (17)
James Allen's Girls' School,
Dulwich, London
(Gold Medal Award winner)
1990

Rugby League: as expected

Nocker Norton,
Balding albino tiger,
The Boulevard mud
Does not lust for your body
As expected.

The inevitable massive tackle
Does not spread its muddy, muscled grasp
Around another passive Titan
As expected.

The humpty dumpty ball
Does not, when in your arms,
Smell another odious armpit
As expected.

But instead flashes like
A laser beam from
Your tinkling fingertips.
The crowd
Loves you
As expected.

David Woodhouse (14)
(Award winner)
1984

'American Footballers'
Gary Butt (14)
1986

Yorkshire

Flint walls cuts
the puckered land,
Crag houses have splintered and thrust up
out of the dark earth,
they squat uneasily on the hillsides

A countryside of bog and moor,
mist and drizzle,
Its people rise up
out of ditches
and its slow heart beats
in the roots of the damp heather

Emma Payne (16)
Hackney, London
(Award winner)
1985

How strange

How strange . . .
While wet snow falls,
The daffodils bloom.

The sky is blank. Emotionless. Concealing secrets.
I sit watching from the window.
The daffodils are fresh clear cut and the
    surroundings blurred, out of focus.

A bird flies across the sky
Quickly, it wants to get into shelter.
It doesn't fit into the picture
Too fast, too fast,
The rest is slow, asleep
A moment frozen in time

Strange . . .

Ruth Leader (13)
(Highly commended)
1984

A siesta

The little black ant,
Determined as ever,
Crawls over my finger.
As he reaches the top,
He turns and looks up at me,
Smiling wisely to himself.

Mummy is stretched out
On the grey prickly rug,
Her hat pulled over her eyes.
Her hair is entwined
With the blades of grass,
Glistening in the sun.

There's a daisy right in front of my nose,
With a drop of dew on one petal.
A sparkling spider's web
Is stranded from it,
To a nearby companion.

Sheba bounds over to me,
Her eyes bright and evil.
Her black fur is warm and soft
As she pounces on my leg.
She sits down
On the edge of the rug
And carefully preens a whisker.
Her deep purr sounds.

I can hear a bird
Twittering furiously
In an overhead tree.
It swoops down into sight.
Sheba watches the little bird's antics
With a half-opened eye.

My back is getting sticky,
My bonnet's irritating me.
I let out a cry,
Startling Sheba, waking Mummy.
She slowly stirs.
'Shush, darling,
Time to go in.'
Her voice coos softly.

I'm hoisted over a hip,
And I bury my face
In her soft pullover.
It tastes nice.
I watch her hair swing,
Back and forth,
Back and forth.
My eyes close,
And the world drifts out.

Emily Wilson (13)
Sidcot School,
Winscombe, Avon
(Highly commended)
1985

Who is living next door?

The removal men come and go:
Like yo-yos their strings get entangled.
Packing cases pile themselves in acrobatic poses,
Lions jump through hoops all around them.
Bees busying about their chores,
In the compact hive next door.
A voice of thunder crashes around the echoing rooms,
The sun cringes,
And cowers behind a cloud.
A tumble of words
Spilling out,
Rippling over my ears.
A waterfall of foreign phrases,
Twisting themselves into patterns.
They mean nothing to me.
A splash of distorted English,
Then the flow stops,
Dripping only occasionally.
The removal men disperse.
The house stands silent,
Then the screen door opens,
And a cracking voice
From the record player begins to sing . . .
'Mein hit der hat drei echen . . .'

A serpent begins to slither from inside the house,
A long leg encased in khaki trousers,
And tall black wartime boots.
My new neighbour breathes in deeply,
My eyes are elastic
And stretch open to breaking point.
His eyes fall on mine,
My own snap back into shape.
My body is in the Arctic,

My mind in England.
That moustache!
Those eyes!
That hair!
It is him.
He smiles,
His front teeth are cracked,
His voice cracks the air,
'You want some candy, little girl?'
My feet jump mindlessly to attention.

Helen Bright (14)
Torpoint, Cornwall
(Silver Medal Award Winner)
1991

A television crew in my room

This morning I woke to find a television crew in my
    room.
They weren't there last night when I turned out the
    light.
The producer is on the bunk bed bossing the crew
    around.
There's a man filming up on the light.
'Action.'
'Roll.'

There's a desperate chase round the bedroom.
I decide it's best to crawl under my bed.
Oh no, there's a polar bear here, he's in the next scene.

Nadia Bagwell (9)
Freda Gardham C. P. School,
Rye, Sussex
1986

The polar bear

The polar bear's
fur is
like sugar.
His nose
is like a
black plum.

Jason Fields (9)
New Milton
Junior School,
Hants
1985

Frogs in water

There was a splash when the frogs
Jumped in the water.
   A ripple,
   A wobble,
   A stir.
They are deaf to the songbirds
   but
When the rain comes down
And pats the water as if it were a dog,
The frogs gently listen.

Andrew Abbott (10)
Beaudesert Park School,
Stroud, Glos.
1986

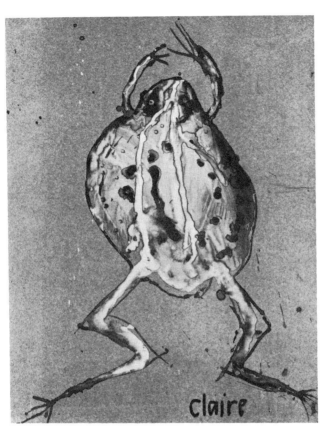

'Toad'
Clare Savage (7)
1985

A bat

A bat
Flaps like a rag
At night.

Matthew Rowland (11)
All Saints' Middle School,
Sudbury, Suffolk
1990

'Sam'
Lynsey Foster (6)
1983

My cat

My cat walks carefully,
It stretches each leg,
Not a sound
No claws
Just soft paws.
It creeps to a bird
And waits.
It jumps
Fast
Like a spring.

Kelly Griffin (8)
Barton Hill
Primary School,
Bristol
1986

The midnight fox

When the night is young
And is waiting to be used,
To be blown, to be sounded,
The orange fox with moonlight eyes
Prowls,
Snooping, with nostrils quivering
As the wind disturbs quiet smells that hide in the
cloak of the shadows,
And he smiles.

Michael Duggan (12)
Beckenham, Kent
1988

Dog dozes

Curled up.
Crouched, like a muffin
In front of the fire,
To toast.

Electric glow
Darts her eyes.
Heat absorbed,
Cold light flashed back.

Nose on wrist
She ponders.
Eyes close.
Her mind slinks away.

Helen Rahman (14)
Chorley, Lancs
1988

I Think a Lot

Grown-ups!

My Dad says,
'Timothy,
TIMOTHY!
Are you listening?'
'Yes Dad . . .'
'Look at me when I'm talking to you!'
'Yes Dad.'
'How many times have I told you?'
Too many
'If I've told you once I've told you a thousand times.'
'Yes Dad.'

My Mum says,
'BORED?
In my day we were never bored.
We didn't know the meaning of the word!
We didn't have time to be bored.'
'Yes Mum . . .'
'CAN'T?
There's no such word as can't!
Young people today don't know how lucky they are!
We never dreamt of owning a car.'
'Yes Mum.'

My teacher says,
'Are you listening to me?'
'Yes Miss . . .'
'You'll never learn anything if you don't listen.'
'Yes Miss.'
'Don't answer back!'
'Yes Miss.'

I listen,
I don't speak,
But I think a lot.

Timothy Dimon (11)
Allertonshire School,
Northallerton, North Yorkshire
1991

Thoughts

All people that on Earth do dwell,
Hope Mr Foster isn't in a bad mood,
Wonder if he's here yet?
Bet he's having his breakfast,
Come ye before him and rejoice.

The piano's wobbly,
Might fall over,
Without our aid he did us make,
Hope Mr Foster's ill,
And for his sheep he doth us take,

O enter then his gates with praise,
Latin room's empty,
Approach with joy his courts unto,
I'm in detention today,
Have to write out 100 lines,
For it is seemly so to do.

Marcus Holburn (10)
(Highly commended)
1983

'Old Master'
Peter Kelly (17)
(Italian Tour Award winner)
1988

Philip's poem

The day is like an elastic band
It stretches out longer and longer
When I'm at school.
But when the evening comes
It snaps back
Before I have time to play.

Philip Gradidge (8)
Chandlers Ford, Hampshire
(Silver Medal Award Winner)
1991

There's someone in our class . . .

There's someone.In our class who cannot.
Write in sentences our.Teacher keeps saying
write.In decent sentences a sentence is.
A group of words that makes complete.Sense.
But this.Someone never.Listens !

Their's somion inn or clas ho canknot spel proupirlei.
He as the mosst auful spileing nowlidge.
Mrs Catlledinner ses it's dubble ditch.
But thiss somion niver lissteenss !

There'ssomeoneinourclasswhoneverleavesafingerspace
betweenwords.MrsCastledinedoesnotapproveofhiswriting.
Shesaysshemusthaveverythinfingers.
Butthissomeoneneverlistens!

There's someone in our class
who writes too big.
He tries to write small
but he hasn't got the knack yet.
This someone is a very small person –
not like his writing !

There's someone in our class who cannot concentrate.
This someone finds it very difficult to . . .
'What was I saying ?'

Marcus Throup (11)
Sandiacre Cloudside County Junior School,
Sandiacre, Nottingham
(Silver Medal Award winner)
1990

Jigsaw

Some people are incomplete
like an unfinished jigsaw
A picture left imperfect.

Some make their own piece
to fill the gap
Improvising with their 'artistic' eye.
Others are clever
they smile and laugh
letting their twinkling manner guide a
probing eye away.

But many just
lie broken.
Gaping,
Waiting and hoping
someone will find the last piece for them.

Magda Hewitt (16)
Billericay School,
Billericay, Essex
(Highly commended)
1989

'Marathon '83'
Alistair Provan (11)
(Highly commended)
1984

Discipline

One times one is three.
Six times seven is forty two.
Battle of Hastings: 1066
      Answer!
Grey dawn outside.

Who was the first disciple?
Define a primary source.
Hydrogen, helium, lithium . . .
        Answer!
Cloudy morning outside.

A quadrilateral is a four-sided shape.
An adjectival phrase describes a noun.
Eight quavers in a four-four bar.
        Answer!
Rain slithers outside.

Je suis, tu es, il est . . .
Repetition intensifies descriptive passages.
Denote recessive genes: *b*.
        Answer!
Stormy afternoon outside.

One of the themes of the play is gemstones.
Use the subjunctive with *il faut*.
Dress carefully for interviews.
        Answer!
Shadowed twilight outside.

Have you done last week's accounts?
Where is the Brown file?
Don't forget to clock in.
        Answer!
Weekend. Paycheque.
Darkness falls outside.

Claire Milne (15)
Urmston, Manchester.
(Italian Tour Award winner)
1988

The nature of man

A jug of chemicals
for an interview?

He lined himself,
as a bowerbird does his nest,
to better his rival.

Only to be ranked
as chickens
and twisted
like an ivy.
To creep along
the chosen wall.

Claire Davis (13)
Newcastle-under-Lyme School,
Newcastle-under-Lyme, Staffs
(Arthur Lines Poetry Award
winner)
1989

There are many things

There are many things which we can fear
Spiders, dark nights, walking home
Alone.
The threat of war.
Closed spaces, open
Spaces. Death.

There are many things which we can think of
Questions, answers, memories
And the smell of toast.

Buttercups in summer fields, daisies
In a vase, the birds
Singing. Chocolate fudge.

There are many things
We only fear
Because we think.

Imagine
The fear of buttered toast,
The happy thought of darkness.

Maybe what we fear most is our thoughts.

There are many things we can think we fear
Spiders, dark chocolate, walking birds
Alone.
The threat of fudge.
Closed buttercups, open
Daisies. Death.

There are many things
We only think
Because we fear.

Imagine
The happy thought of war,
The fear of buttered memories.

Maybe what we fear most is ourselves.

Catherine Wilkinson (17)
Buckden,
Huntingdon, Cambridgeshire
(Individual Gold Medal Award winner)
1991

'Tough As Old Boots'
Nicholas Brady (15)
1985

Not hero: Hell's Angel

The tranquillity and peace is torn asunder
With a resounding battle-cry of throbbing thunder;
An exulting fanfare challenging all and none,
Metal charger gleaming in the sun.
Hard boots, hard drugs, hard life and harder eyes,
Hell's Angel – discarded dregs, despaired of and
　　despised.
Leather jacket taut across his back,
Like hair and coat and bike his character is black.
Demon rider, he crouches on his monstrous steed,
Ripping down the road at careless speed.
Hell's Angel – a fiend in human form,
Hell's Angel – a devil lacking horns.
He sees her twisted marble, frightened face
Frozen by fear in endless time and space.
The bike sloughs round, its fabric ripped apart with
　　tortured squeal,
Hard tree, hard ground, hard life, hard death, hard deal.

He died that she might live yet who would name
Nick Riley hero – who'd press his claim?
He was a Hell's Angel, thus sealed his fate –
Not Nick Riley, hero: but Hell's Angel, late.

Jannine Jobling (14)
Barton-upon-Humber,
South Humberside
1986

Not for Him

Not for Him a big white ambulance,
But a slow donkey.
Not for Him flashing blue lights,
But the star of Bethlehem.
Not for Him the white hospital wards,
But a cold stable.
Not for Him a nice warm cradle,
But a manger full of straw.
Not for Him fleecy babygros,
But plain swaddling bands.
Not for Him the Midwife, Nurse and Doctors,
But three simple shepherds.
Not for Him Auntie and Uncle from the North,
But three Kings from the East.
Not for Him a cuddly teddy bear,
But a shepherd boy's lamb.
Not for Him a silver coin in his palm,
But Frankincense, Myrrh and Gold.
Not for Him a future in computers,
But the crown of Heaven.

Daniel Salcedo (11)
(Highly commended)
1983

Silent night fever

October,
yes, Your Royal Hypeness,
the push has begun.
Load up your bags with some festive filled fun.
Santa
Claus bared.
Kids hooked
and snared.
Urge to buy, to have, to hold.
'Sorry Sir, good cheer was sold.'
M & S 'Penny Bazaar',
trouble is they never are.
Oh, the spirit of the occasion:
mainly Martini in my estimation.
But the press aren't
out of the gutter.
Headline news of the
Queen's pre-speech stutter.
Now follow the weeks
of special programmes.
Minds to the slaughter
like biblical lambs.
Material gain of presents galore.
Girls' plastic dolls and boys' plastic war.
Silent night fever,
the time bomb's in store.

Alison Pember (16)
The Grove School, St Leonards on Sea
East Sussex
(Highly commended)
1989

We apologize for the fault in transmission

In the House of Commons today
There was
SURPRISE!
On both sides of the chamber,
When a backbench MP
No one had ever heard of,
Announced his decision
To go and take a running jump
Into the Thames.

In an emotional address
He ended a three-year run
Of completely meaningless talk.

Figures released today indicate
The trend towards complete
Public indifference continues . . .

> I need to communicate.
> Who will pull down this wall of words?
> I cannot escape my head,
> I cannot be you.
> Where is the feeling,
> The understanding I need to talk with?

. . . with lines of emotion cut,
Nothing is getting through.
Contact is impossible
And the situation looks likely to worsen.

But now for the weather . . .

Nicholas Perks (17)
Dalkeith, Mid Lothian
1991

Trivialities

Why do more buses always go past,
On the other side of the road?
Why do people always manage to arrive a minute before
The bus you've been waiting hours for?
Why does nobody tell you it's one of the main functions
in life?
Eating, drinking, sleeping, going on the loo, and waiting
for buses.
Mozart probably could have written another concerto,
If he didn't have to keep waiting for the number twelve.
Scott would have probably been the first to the Pole,
If his bus hadn't got held up in snow-storms:
Why is it that the buses have to go on strike,
And leave you stranded in the middle of nowhere,
When you have an exam you've actually revised for?
What's the use of a philosophical thirteen year old girl
Who just can't accept
The trivialities of life?

Jade Widocks (13)
Bolton School Girls Division, Bolton
(Highly commended)
1989

Are feathers better than umbrellas?

Up Heatherside, rainy, cold
I waited by the bus stop.
Near to me a girl
Covered in feathers
I tried to make conversation –
'What time's the next bus?'
'How much is a return?'
She grunted
I tried
To make conversation –
'Cold, isn't it?'
She grunted
I tried
'Are feathers better than umbrellas,
Do they keep you dry?'
She grunted
I wished I'd taken an earlier bus.

Kerry Pope (15)
Tomlinscote School,
Frimley, Surrey
(Silver Medal Award Winner)
1991

Life

Life is like a fancy dress costume.
I wonder, Who wore it before us?

Charlotte Little (14)
1984

'Me in My Yellow Wellies'
Alison Pickford (10)
Daven County Junior School,
Congleton, Cheshire
(Highly commended)
1989

Almost extinct

There is a zoo
At the end of the universe.
A creature with flesh,
Two eyes and some hair
Sits on its own.
'What is it?' they ask.
'It is a human;
The only one left;
The rest are dead,
Along with their world.
They fought each other
And killed all the animals.
They strangled the corn
With nooses of roundabouts,
Playgrounds for cars.
Space meals were eaten.
They all fell ill.'
There is a zoo
At the end of the universe
Where the last human sits
Looking at space.

Jonathan Hart (13)
Debenham High School,
Stowmarket, Suffolk
(Cadbury's Gold Award for Schools)
1991

Love So Surprise?

Love so surprise?

When in the wind is the where?
With the blue-eyes, the you-eyes,
And with the so wind in your hair
So golden, so random surprise?

Whither your lips so red,
Which meet mine in when and in where?
What words my lips so said
So lost in the random-wind there?

So love-lost in purple heather, or
Who else in the world so fair
Or cheek so smooth, or law
Of Nature surprise in the care?

When the You and the wind in the heather
With me, lips, words of Us love?
Is Nature random, so together
The Us and the so clouds above?

Is love in your eyes, You so fair?
Above us the random cloud wise?
Whither the random when and the where?
My nature – love you – so surprise?

Jon Harley (16)
Barnard Castle, Co. Durham
(Highly commended)
1985

'Tears for the Sea'
Lucy Campbell (12)
Kilgraston School
Bridge of Earn,
Perthshire
1990

One day

One day I fell in love.
It was just like a butterfly
Emerging from its chrysalis;
So beautiful, I cried.
It was a bite
Out of an apple,
So sweet its juice
Tasted like honey.
It was a tiny
Baby fist,
Clutching a strand of hair;
A golden thread.
It was a rainbow
Of more than seven colours,
Millions and millions.
One day I fell in love
And I grew wings;
I flew. Briefly

I was a bird,
An eagle, flying
Up and up.
One day, one smile
Meant more to me
Than the whole world.
One day, I sang.
All day, I sang.
But then
My butterfly died
And the apple grew old.
The fist let go of the thread,
The golden hair.
My rainbow
Shattered into
A myriad
Coloured pieces.
My wings
Disappeared,
And I fell
Down and down.
I couldn't
Even
Sing

Then,
One day,

I fell in love.

Rachael Anne-Marie Naylor (14)
(Highly commended)
1983

A time for love

I love you
swinging   every second
wound up   ready to spring
moving   anti-clockwise
ringing   in my ears

I love you

waking   ☐
working   ☐
laughing   ☐
drinking   ☐
crying   ☐
sleeping   ☐
always   ☐

Please tick   inside me

Anna Pegler (16)
Billericay, Essex
1985

Rose

Red rose, red rhythmed rose,
Red tooth-mugged ripe rhythmed rose
Is pulsing, quick, on my rose-shelf.

The room seems full of petals,
Red, red, red rose petals, and
They sing upon the floor.
My eyes, perhaps, are petals:
Red with love, pulsating: petals.

O there is a young, blush, red rose
Vivid in my tooth-mug:

                    no one has seen her
Save me:
          my eyes which, like rose's
Red eye, she brightens and bares.

James Loxley (16)
Epping, Essex
(Highly commended)
1985

Aeroplane

I will be your aeroplane,
    twisting, turning, swooping, gliding,
you can pull my controls,

    and I will do tricks for you,
I will dive, dip and rise high to the clouds

    and turn upside down,
I will be your
                    aeroplane.

Claire Bayntun (9)
Freda Gardham C. P. School,
Rye, Sussex
1986

'Pressure (City on my Back)'
Carol Day (17)
1984

Untitled

And it seems that I have grown
Not so much cynical
As too analytical;
Too questioning; too near
To answers that will not satisfy.
I shall not love you:
I dare not love you.

One day I will lose you,
And in my sorrow send you poetry,
Proclaiming that this is love;
Lyrically bemoaning how a paradise was lost;
Claiming your affections
Off-set all my own confusions.
But I will be lying.
The itinerant minstrel,
Selfishly perpetrating
Both half-truths and untruths,
To satisfy his own remorseful conscience.
I tell you now,
I do not love you:
I dare not love you.

You will find me clumsy; careless;
More than a little absent-minded.
And what I tend to lose
Is what I tend to hold most dear to me.
Do not entrust me with anything precious.
I grow afraid to gamble
If the stakes should rise too high –
My hand cannot be that strong.
I do not love you.
Simply because I dare not love you.

Stephen Lee (17)
The Aelfgar Centre,
Rugeley, Staffs
(Highly commended)
1987

In and out of Joyce's daydream

One and one is two,
Two and two is four,
Three and three are the times I
watched the weakness in your wandering eye waver
as lovers for the first times two kissed, without a
care.
Two times two is four,
Three times three is the smoothness of
your skin is so sublime times nine is seventy-two days
now you have gone. I wanted to tell you how I, don't
    know the answer,
miss your loving gaze.
I stare at your empty seat.

'James! 12 times 11 is 132.'
'Yes miss' you.

Darren Bowget (14)
Mintlaw, Aberdeenshire
1985

Prostitute

Petals of the flower
Part revealing white
   uneven teeth.
Her lips were deliciously
Smug in red,
I want her, the men said.
(But I wanted her.)
She had a baby, they said,
Brown it was, touch of the
Tarbrush, they said.
(I loved her baby.)
She cried only once,
like a dull shower of
Rain over her teacup.
Stupid cow, they said
Was always complaining
She never slept.
Now she sleeps alone and
   Cold.
And I cried at the funeral,
Holding her
Brown Baby.

Giovanna Iazzi (15)
Trinity Catholic High School,
Woodford Green, Essex
1989

Waiting for a rose

(dedicated to Shelley Page)

He shopping-trolleyed his way
Through the cash-till queue
And handed it to me in a
Waitrose bag.
Crushed
like an unwanted receipt
Of his refrigerated
Affections for me.

Catherine Burkinshaw (16)
Aylesbury, Bucks
(Highly commended)
1988

Snow in May

It is May,
And no one could have forecast
The sudden bleaching of fields,
Birches frozen against the half-light.
This has confused even the blackbirds,
Pondering in their nests;
And I,
Who yesterday
Lay in the sunshine,
Reach for my winter coat.
For once,
I thought that
I'd melted the ice.

But you are in conspiracy
With the sky,
And in this bleak land,
I cannot see the sun penetrating
The frosted grey,
Ever again.

Helen Wightman (16)
Basingstoke, Hants
(Highly commended)
1987

'Landscape with Cows'
Nicola Flockart (16)
1988

Their wedding day

Like snow
Flurries of cold confetti
Fall on the girl
Within a white cage
And freeze the flowers in their prime.
Black, beside her,
Stands the lock to her cage,
So pleased he's the one
To be shutting the door.

Alice Louise Bird (16)
1983

The wedding

She was embarrassed at the church,
She went all red,
And said,
I don't!
WHAT?! came the call from the crowd.
They glared from under their big fancy hats.
Feathers, veils, fruit and all
Shook with shock . . .

Judith Freeth (12)
Priestley Smith School,
Erdington, Birmingham
1986

Corset and Combinations

Combinations tends the rose beds,
Mounds the earth and snips at the grass,
Corset meanwhile starches the curtains,
Vinegars the windows, picks the roses for her class.

Combinations potters in the potting shed,
Measures the nail on which to hang his secateurs,
Corset's eye spies through the latticed window,
Lifts her chin, drops her eyes, sniffs in sharp and briskly
    stirs.

Combinations lifts his watch and wanders down the path,
Wobbles the wobbly fencepost and shows some mild
    concern,
Corset switches pinny from the plain to the poppied one,
Dishes up sprouts and beans and broccoli to each plate in
    turn.

They must be in there, somewhere,
Carefully eating, everything fine,
Never seen, unheard, secretly pinning
Corsets and combinations on the line.

Katie-Louise Thomas (16)
Chelsfield, Kent
(Italian Tour Award winner)
1989

The rivals

He was still there
Crouching over the regimental rows of Begonias
In the half light.
Some people said he was obsessed.
He could not feel her watching him,
But only the lingering dampness in the evening air
And the sweet perfumed companionship of the Roses.
She tried to remember a time
When he had touched her
The way he touched their silken petals.
She wanted to tear the head
From each self-satisfied bloom
And crush it in her hand,
Until it was just a velvet pulp.
Perhaps then he would look up at her,
Into her face,
And listen as his battalion of shrubs cried out
In silent distress –
'It was your wife who destroyed your garden.
Your jealous wife
Who has only flowers to despise.'

Kathryn Simmonds (16)
Digswell, Welwyn, Herts
(Highly commended)
1989

Public opinion

We met in nineteen forty nine,
And I still get a shiver down my spine
Every time he holds my hand.
Being in love is really grand.

He works on the London Stock Exchange.
The first gift he gave me was the 'Filofax' range.
I love his eyes and his brand new car.
Being in love is super, ya.

I met my fella on an aeroplane,
When we was coming back from Spain.
He works in Wimpy on Peckham High Street.
Being in love is really neat.

He has the most perfect face I've seen,
His teeth are white, his hair is clean,
And even though we're still at school,
Being in love is mega-cool.

We met at a rally for saving the whale,
We both got arrested and put into jail.
Last Christmas he bought me a white kaftan.
Being in love is way out, man.

We live in the same block of council flats,
We met when he helped me get rid of the rats.
He's got some money, but not a lot,
So being in love is all we've got.

Sarah Cohen (14)
Ealing, London
1991

Tears the
Heartstrings

The fist descended

the fist
descended
the sickening crunch
the snapping limb
the stifled scream
that tears the heartstrings

(but no one moves)
the shout of anger
the dripping tear
(but no one moves)
the pleading,
the hate,
(but no one moves)
not my business
nothing to do with me

(still no one moves)
until
the misplaced
blow

the final destruction.
neighbours appear
the child, a
shrunken corpse
in death
lies prone
horrified
indignant;

appalled
neighbours

phone
the police

contented
the neighbours
disperse
'i've done my duty'

but what about
the child
dear contented
neighbours
it's dead dear
neighbours;

and you were too late
dear neighbours

again.

Guy Soar (16)
(Highly commended)
1983

The homecoming

She waited in fear,
For his homecoming.
While he drank his beer
He thought nothing of her.
The doorbell rang with impatience.
Startled, she jumped up in terror,
Slowly the chain was unlatched
And there he stood, anger in his eyes.
Walking backwards into the kitchen,
Tears flowing from her eyes,
He followed removing his
Thick, black, leather belt.

He lashed out at her, with joy;
She dared not scream;
The children were upstairs;
Too late feet pattered along the floor.
She had seen their lonely far away look,
The terror in their eyes.
Slowly they left.
Knowing what was happening.

Rachel Nixon (14)
Marist Convent Senior School,
Fulham, London
1986

Violation

Avenue of foliage
With debris of morn
Hugged her as she leisured from school.
She felt in her pockets,
Cigarette end, lights to life,
Calming her from tutoring tension.

But within the walls of the leafy tunnel
Lurked the 'little girl dreamer',
The 'little girl exterminator'.
Like the owl in its trunk, out he looked,
But when looked upon,
Hidden owl becomes 'He'.

Female ears didn't twitch,
No breaking of twig.
She didn't even sense.
Why should she?

Girl . . .
Journey almost ended.
Man . . .
End of tether,
His mouth dry;
Like his stomach, his conscience growled.
Withdrawal symptoms crept in.

Bird of prey flew swiftly,
With whispering wings
And gliding ease.
Victim drawn to talons.
Vortex thoughts within girl's mind.
'Scream! Scream!'
But silent scream
Caused from the metacarpus clamp.

After he's finished, what does he do?
He leaves her,
Scarlet threads around her throat.
He can't afford to let her tell
For he enjoyed it
And he will enjoy it again.
For he is the germ;
The world is the breeder,
Spawning this bacteria
To infect the human race.

What can be done?
Unlike the owl, it will never be extinct,
A helix built upon a million others,
It can not be erased,
Quenched or destroyed.

Aston Hart (14)
Debenham High School,
Stowmarket, Suffolk
(Highly commended)
1987

'The Crow
and the Snail'
Natasha
Davies (7)
Hayle,
Cornwall
1990

He didn't mean it, officer

When he jumped
he didn't mean
to splatter his remains
on the ground.

I knew him, officer,
He was my friend.
He didn't mean to
actually
kill himself.

It was just that he
read somewhere
that not deciding not to live
was in effect saying
'I want to stay alive.'

But he felt he'd never
actually decided,
only drifted into
being
still here.

He didn't mean it, officer,
when he jumped.
But when he realized
he had the power
to take the decision
to end his life,
he wanted to know
how it felt
to feel the power
to take the decision.

So, he took the decision
and jumped.
and realized,
too late,
he couldn't decide
not to . . .
after all!

So,
having decided
to decide,

He died.

Helen King (15)
Chantry High School,
Ipswich, Suffolk
1986

The Queen has tooth trouble

Newsflash,   bang
We are receiving reports   bang
    receiving reports   bang
    receiving reports,   bang
                                                bang
One,   bang
Two suspected dead,   bang
       Three. bang
Four bombs,   bang
Audio images.   bang
Carnage.   Holocaust.   bang

Sullen putrefaction.

the IRA telephoned our Dublin office claiming
  responsibility

A deeper cut,
Pouring salt into the nail wound.
Responsibility is a big word.
They are responsible
For making people see.

And shattering the peace.

The bandstand – Regent's Park
Will not be the same again.
the band were playing tunes from the popular musical
  Oliver

Six bandsmen were playing
Popular tunes.
They
Are as dead as

Everybody.

But they now see why.
Just the
Click . . . Click . . . Click . . .
As the needle grooves on endlessly.
The auto-reject has failed again,
And the bodies
Lie around,
Like paper cutouts
Blown over in a strong wind.

Kevin David Andrews (17)
(Highly commended)
1983

Heroes

A man can only die once
But a hero can, and must, die many times.
The everyday person falls every day
Unnoticed, ignoble, but with dignity.
A hero does not die every day
But his death is repeated
To remind the minds of the nation;
They're paralysed,
Fleetingly,
But over and over again.

Five hundred ordinary men die
Together; and the nation reels
But the next day boards a jet and forgets.
Seven heroes die
And the film reels unwind
As millions mourn for themselves;
They need to see tears to remember how to cry.
Until the memory fades in time
Like the parachute of hope they saw
Falling over and over again.

Twisted bodies hauled from mangled wreckage
The country winces – and turns away.
They weren't there at the time so it's not important.
A fireball in the sky, live on television,
The nation goes into shock.
But the press want to know
What the President said,
And can't accept silence
At a 'major malfunction',
Asking over and over again.

Sophie Kyle (17)
Slough, Bucks
1986

152

Poppy

A shout,
Like a machine gun, rattles
Across a barren waste
Where nothing moves
And spiders spin
Gigantic webs
Of sprawling steel
That twist and tangle,
Tear and rip
The ragged wind.
And on that wind
Floats a solitary grain
Of amber and grey,
Spiralling down
To be consumed
By lakes of rust.
It sleeps in the sludge
And lies, like a mine,
Waiting for a touch.
With a burst, it explodes,
Throwing tongues of flame
That do not burn.
And, when they die,
They leave behind
More seeds to bloom
For all mankind.

Tony Roberts (13)
Debenham High School,
Debenham,
Stowmarket, Suffolk
1989

Borderlines

He saw them right enough.
His mind went Border Patrol
As he searched for his licence.
But in his heart thumped
A peculiar pain as they
Swarmed around the headlamps.
He didn't make a move, not yet,
He wasn't sure if he'd heard
Alright and anyway the cold
Steady drizzle put him off
On a night when he should
Be by a good turf fire.
And so they opened the cab
Door to wrench him out
In one firm, cloying grasp.
He looked and thought to
See a hardened Catholic face
With black beret and sleeked eye
But saw instead a blond man,
Disinterested and with a green
Muffler. One shot blasted
Him into the sodden ditch.
They found him later and
His cattle truck; they cleaned
Him up so people admired his
Neat grey coffin suit but
Avoided looking at the
Mess where his face had been.

Rosemary Cowan (17)
Co. Londonderry, N. Ireland
(Award winner)
1985

'Conway Mill Belfast'
Ruth Mulvenna (17)
(Italian Tour Award winner)
1988

I'm scared

I'm scared
The throng is loaded into the car,
like dirt being shovelled into a hole.
We fill the gaps and consume
the sticky, smelly, sweaty air.
Buttonholes of light struggle into the crowded, noisy car.
Where is my family?

I'm scared
There's my Mother, paralysed by her pride.
She will not let salty tears stain her dirty face.
We're trapped like beasts in a cage.

I'm scared.

Nea Bayley (14)
John Kyrle High School, Ross-on-Wye,
Herefordshire
1989

Belsen

The chandeliers glistened and turned to music
And while the men danced
Their cups overflowed
And amid the Golden Apple
The core rotted.

The huts, drab and grey,
Stood lifeless as the bodies
Strewn, decaying like the vanquished
In sick and pointless war.
The silence deafened.

Those that walked
Spread their skin on their bodies as best they could,
Paper people, searching mounds of dead for food.
Caged humans,
Caged animals.

The wind rattled among them,
Spitting disease.

When the animals were freed from their cages.
When the cruelty ceased,
When the huts were burned,
Hell remained.

Patrick Brothers (14)
The King's School,
Canterbury, Kent
1986

Life in East Berlin?

6.15 a.m.
I woke to hear a gunshot,
Murdering the silence of dawn.
I looked out
Of my uncurtained window
To see a guard
On the wall
Aim
And take another shot.
I followed the line of his fire –
Some poor bastard
Was lying in the river
Dying,
Then the shot
That he would never hear
Killed me
A little more.

Roy Biddle (14)
(Highly commended)
1984

'Richmond Street, Penzance'
Bruce Le Grange (17)
(Highly commended)
1985

Beirut — a day in the death of

(To those of the Sabra and Chatila camps, alive and dead,
hoping that nothing similar will happen again)

Life stirred —
The sun rose, birds sang.
The soldier shifted slightly,
Stretched and yawned, leant
His gun against his other shoulder.
Behind the crumbling wall
Smiling, shrill-voiced mothers called.
Playing happily,
Their children wouldn't come.
Seven ages chattered, cried;
All seven ages to be destroyed.
The soldier coughed, his throat gone dry . . . But
He spoke a different language,
Wouldn't hear their pleas, when he let
That army in among them,
Like hunting hounds unleashed.

A movement in the corner of his eye,
Lorries, driving slowly, crowded faces,
Guns.   A sight he would deny.
They marched towards
The open gates,
The talking, trusting people.
Just keeping order — no biblical sin —
He reassured his conscience.
Nausea rising, he turned away.

Inside, a job was being done:
Knives flashed, guns flared.
Initial reluctance being passed
One can murder methodically;
It can be done with no feeling,
The manual had said,
Forgetting to mention
The long, drawn-out screams.
Some run, some fight,
Concealing fear and hatred.
Bodies pile up. The sun goes down.
Spotlights flood the camp,
Leaving no dark corners to hide.
The soldiers scribble graffiti
With knives; on bodies.
Mothers, babies,
Both are slaughtered.
On into the night . . .
Eyes glazed, he saw his future:
Discussion of his case –
Shellshock, you know. We cannot
Understand. He only witnessed
Extermination of laughing, living people.
Again the sun rose –
Red as blood –
Nothing stirred.

Lara Burns (15)
(Highly commended)
1984

Dead in Libya

They found him
Under the rubble.

The Americans had thought it
A good idea
To bomb the city.
To stop the terrorists
They used the planes
From Lakenheath
'With British approval,
Of course'.
With whose approval?
None of us
Was asked.

But what about the little boy?
What had he done
Wrong?
It was not he
Who had sent the bomb,
So why
Was it his corpse there
Under the rubble?

Victoria Rudd (14)
Debenham High School,
Stowmarket, Suffolk
1987

Earth child

Born of earth,
this brittle child of clay
baked by the sun kiln;
a thin figure rolled in mud,
fired in blistering heat,
this earth child, son of
rainless desert,
dust-child, shell-spattered.

Only in his eyes
is the soil moist;
and here it is stolen
by flies that crawl
like thieves
across the cracked chasm
of lips that bleed air.

Feed him rain;
Let his parchment-thin body
soak up liquid, breathe water.

Soften the cracked clay.

Siobhan Aiton (15)
Ysgol Gyfun, Llangefni (Llangefni
Comprehensive School)
Anglesey, Gwynedd
(Italian Tour Award winner)
1988

Romanian orphans

Overcrowded, in bleak rooms,
Dirty, in unmattressed cots,
Lie silent children without a future.

Catherine McKeary (11)
Coleraine High School,
Coleraine, County Londonderry
1991

Entreaty

(For the women of Kuwait who refused to allow their
relatives to fight against Iraq. November 1990)

Not in my name, brother, not in my name.
She is a heroine who sends her brothers there
to fight and die, but I will never be one.
She will call me coward, she who never flinches
to see them going, but if you kill in my name
you kill the one who bears it.
Take not my honour to the battle ground
to bring back stained with blood, I will deny it.
I will deny it and accept the shame,
rather than bear, until my death, one death.
Even if that death be yours, I have chosen, brother.
I will desert you, and I will die alone.

My brother, if your ghost can cross the sea,
whisper reproaches to me while I sleep,
tell of your killing and your death for me,
I feel the tears, I know how I shall weep;
but then, when you are past all praise or blame,
I will answer – No, brother. Not in my name.

Rachel Muers (15)
Rugby, Warwickshire
(Silver Medal and Most Promising Individual Award winner)
1991

'Portrait of the Valleys'
Angela Jones (14)
1986

Nuke

Watch the sky.
I am coming from out of the shadow.

You will feel my flame, and laugh.
    I, who am Death, have come to you.
I will be swift, and there will be no pain.
    I am forged by your folly.
I come to cleanse.
    I, who am Death, shall ravage your fertile earth.
I come to purge.
    I, who am Death, shall destroy you.
I come to sterilize.
    I, who am Death, shall haunt your children.
Embrace me with a prayer.
    Do not forget me; I AM ARMAGEDDON.

Watch the sky . . .
And fear.

Sam Leith (12)
Downsend School,
Leatherhead, Surrey
1987

'Nuclear Bombed House', group work
Woodside County Primary School,
Oswestry, Shropshire
1983

I Give You Leaves

October

I give you nuts in cloaks of green
I give you berries black and red
Conkers, polished bright and clean
Dropping down from overhead.
In the fields for you I grow
Mushrooms at the dawn of day
And on the hedges high and low
Old mans beard, soft and grey.
I give you leaves of red and gold
I bid the ivy spread its honey,
And though my nights are long and cold
My autumn days are sweet and sunny.

Timothy David Neale (8)
1983

'Twigs and Berries'
Nichola George (7)
(Highly commended)
1986

Harvest walk

Come with me.
Come for a walk.
The apple trees are bending.
They are telling me
That Harvest has come.
They are saying
That their fruit is ripe.
The fish are somersaulting
Out of the lake
To catch the flies.
The dragonflies fly
Around my head.
The corn in the cornfield
Sways in the breeze.

Craig Stovold (6)
Bedgrove County First School,
Aylesbury, Bucks
1987

Autumn wind

The summer leaves know their fate.
As the wind blows through the patchwork quilt
Of copper, crimson and chestnut,
They change their jade jackets
Into crisp autumn coats,
Tailor made for autumn.

Victoria Parkins (12)
Debenham High School,
Stowmarket, Suffolk
(Cadbury's Gold Award for Schools)
1991

November

And so, once more, the wood seems dead.
Scattered with relics of its summer beauty.
And the trees are grey like pillars,
Standing in the stone hall of time.

Alyson McGaw (13)
Wirral County Grammar School for Girls,
Wirral, Merseyside
1988

Sea swan

Swan flew heavy
over the sea,
clapped white wings in the wind:
snake-neck straight.

Snow swan
settled, pressing on the water;
    watching the faces
of young girls less white than his feathers.
    Grey against grey,
the sea and sky met dull as morning
upon Wales.

Low in the tide,
    two islands
echoed with hollow bird-cries:
January-bare.

Night-dark, in the hills
Fann swims among the reeds;
neck gold-banded.
Present in dreams;
she calls to her mate.

And at Moonset
two swans dawn on the water,
ringed in blue-gold;
part of someone's madness.

Like the swan on our sea,
they unfurl their wings to fly,
    leaving only a ripple on still water.

Sarah Lucy Davies (15)
(Award winner)
1983

'Birdwatch'
Karen Dawber (11)
1983

He was rooted

He was rooted
like the oak.
The weather changed
in his veins.
His ears heard the
first phlegm-rattled gasp
of a womb-warm lamb.
His sharp, blue eye
admired Spring's first bud,
gentle as his hands
persuading the udder.
His wind-worn voice
calmed the cow.
His kingdom of
rhythmic fields
was shaped by his love.

Now, his sons are men
with new ideas.
The droning of their machines
drowns the lamb.
Their hedge-cutter slices
the untidy bud.
Their milking machine
forces the udder.
His acres are
shaped by straight wire.

His voice is old
The oak is hacked
from its roots.

Elen Jones (17)
Ysgol Glan-y-Mor, Pwllheli,
Gwynedd
1989

'*End of the Day*'
Wayne Catley (14)
1983

A winter's walk

As we walk along the winter Downs,
The trees, bare of leaves
Stand like skeletons against the cold blue sky, and reveal
    all.
Cradling abandoned nests and little else in their
    windswept branches.

As we trudge along the forest paths,
Last summer's leaves lie trampled in the mud
Black treacle-coloured compost rotting gently in every
    ditch,
While the last remains of January snow thaws in dirty
    patches.

As we struggle with the clinging brambles,
We see trees showing new-born catkins, while below
Brittle twigs snap underfoot and
Frills of velvet fungus spiral long-dead wood.

As we amble back in mud-caked wellies,
The mild winter sunshine warms our wind-chilled faces,
Green shoots struggle through the frosty ground
A promise of summer in our winter's walk.

Sam Mountford (12)
Simonballe School,
Hertford, Herts
1987

Waiting for winter

January is now a missing person.
His description is well . . .
well . . . I suppose
WHITE.
He is dressed in a white suit and hat
and like the Sun he has got it on.
His smile is dazzling white.
Police are anxious to trace him
as he's wanted by many disappointed children.
Has he been kidnapped?
If so Police will be looking
for a gang with frozen fingers.
Is he suffering from amnesia?
Has he flaked out somewhere?
A reward is offered for information
leading to the arrest of January Snow.
Meanwhile a substitute will be taking his place.
She is called April.
This explains the mild weather
which is set to continue
for quite a while.

Julia Wearn (10)
Cloudside County Junior School,
Sandiacre, Nottingham
(Highly commended)
1989

The lambing

Rain tightens the fen margin
To a tremble of high-wire;
Lambs straddle the clover.

Spindly legs splayed,
Struggling on a needle-fine edge
Of earth and sky.

Caul-streaked wool glistens
As warm nostrils heave the air
And damp breath dissolves in the mist.

New-borns flounder in
A comedy of jerk-steps:
A flailing surprise of catfish grins.

And round clown-eyes;
Knees buckle, and elastic turf
Bounces up beneath them.

A fisherman stiffens in mackintosh
To clatter his rods, numb fingers fumbling
The barbed hooks and radish-fat floats.

A switchblade flick, and he casts
A flint arc scattering bite-sparks
On the swollen stream.

Farm ducks abusive,
Petticoat-swaddled washerwomen,
Waddle past the bean rows,

Wade mud-splashed into the pond
And huddle in the weed,
Moaning from the mottled sedge.

Wooden cows dot the neutral flats,
Eyes rolling placidly, tail-switching flies,
Chewing the freshly mown swathes.

Dun lowlands fuse the weather-line
And watersweet meadows spread a yawn
Into the flush of horizon.

Catherine Skinner (16)
Hitchin Girls School,
Hitchin, Herts
(Award winner)
1986

Sunflower

A sunflower is like
A sun puppet on a stick,
Like a round kite
Floating near the ground
Its tail dangling down,
As if someone had
Tied the sun to the soil
So he could see it
Day and night.

Samantha Waters (12)
(Highly commended)
1983

'Sunflower'
Nicola Dobson (7)
1984

Thoughts of a seed

A little boy planted me;
    I feel cool and safe in the soil
    As black as dark.
    I'm thirsty now.
    Who will give me a drink?
    Here comes the rain.
When I push through the soil
    It will be hard,
As hard as a bone.

I want to grow
Into a sunflower, yellow bright.
I want to grow
Up, as high as the clouds.
Then the wind can blow
And bend me;
My seeds will scatter
And the little boy can eat them.
They tell me I need light to grow.
I hope nobody switches off the light.

Ben Thackeray (4), Andrew Pimblott (4),
Paul Armstrong (5), Lauren Eves (5),
Roger Twiss (4), David Cross (4) and
Richard Jones (4)
Ysgol Penmorfa,
Prestatyn, Clwyd
1990

Tree

'What's that?'
The little girl asked
As she sat in the machine.
'I think,' said the man,
'It is a tree,
A relic from
The time of flowers.'
The machine sped on,
Cutting its way
Through the artificial air
In the artificial town.

The tree was trapped,
For tourists' eyes,
In a plastic cage,
Among a mass
Of plastic towers,
Its branches bare;
Its leaves long dead.

Patricia Cope (13)
Debenham High School,
Debenham
Stowmarket, Suffolk
1989

'Garden Centre' Alexander Richardson (7)
Tavistock & Summerhill School, Haywards Heath, West Sussex
1989

Tree

As a child
I looked to the sky
and saw
a riverweed frond
Silhouetted
Against the clouds

Rippling with the
Current of wind
It teased and beckoned
Climb up
On my shoulder
Called the tree

Clasped tight
To the giant's waist
I felt a rocking
Canopy above
Echo through age
Crinkled bark

Spiralling onwards
the slenderest bough
Boasted sights
and excitement
Worthy of heavy breath
and sweat

Crouched on a high
Wooden shoulder
I carved my name
Into the deep
Ochre skin
Deft and proud

I greened over
the raw wound
With a crumpled leaf
but the Tree
shivered
Blood ran sticky yellow
and I cried

Adam Stanley (15)
Minehead, Somerset
(Award winner)
1986

New trees

On the stretch of waste ground over the back
They have planted new trees. Over four miles
Of grassy dips and levels, fifty
To a hundred young saplings scatter: thin
And spindly, swaying in the softest breeze.
   Each alone, they spike the sky-backed rises
   And dot the hollowed levels; each separate
   And frail, they quiver under frozen skies
   While crows, beating like falling water, rise.
The trees remain: frozen in brittle air.

In the short eyeblink of a hundred years
They will still be there, though I will be gone.
By then, the dark earth will be laced with roots
And the sky embroidered with branching twigs:
Day on day will root them more firmly
In local soil, making them a landmark;
And thicker, more straight, they will moan at night,
Become a part of the expected sounds.
   They will become splinters of endurance:
   Remaining, though things around will change;
But by then, I will be dead in earth.

Mark Berry (17)
(Award winner)
1983

Little Jabs of Pain

Logic

Last year
My father died.
It stretched him out
And took his breath
Away clear.
It was so much it
Broke the back
Of reason.

When I find hoards
Of foreign coins,
Or see his books
And pills again,
I leave them back
And dust around those
Little jabs
Of pain

Rosemary Cowan (17)
Co. Londonderry, N. Ireland
(Award winner)
1985

In my house nobody notices

In my house nobody notices,
The little holes in the bath,
The missing biscuits in the pack,
The untold jokes from last year's crackers,
Nobody notices me.

Ruth Ireland (11)
St Anne's CE Middle School,
Bewdley, Worcestershire
1991

January's Child

Too late for summer birth;
Too late even for autumn awakening,
The January Child
Lived out his first days in the cold
And the grey,
With snow on the ground
And frost in the air;
Little wonder that his face was pinched
And his fingers clenched and blue.

Too black and white and grey to survive in the coloured
    summer,
Too austere for pastel springs
And friendly shades;
The January Child
Must hate us so for knowing him
Yet still more bitter is he
When we pass him by.
Little wonder that the child lives as frost
Yet still seeks the warming summer people.

Too innocent and new for earthy passions deep,
Too worldly-wise and old for child-like innocence,
The January Child
Boils inside like molten rock
Yet never melts his ice,
Nor can he quench his thirst.
He weathers like the stone.
Little wonder that he cries
As all the world squeezes blood, and their pound of flesh,
    from him.

Too stubborn for any compromise,
Too yielding to stand as firm support,
He finds no friendship offered
By those who have no sympathy with his
'Other side'.
Watch him grow, twisted yet fine,
Stunted yet strong.
Little wonder that he needs his sharpened shaft
To pierce even those he seems to love, right through to
    the heart.

Too late for softly tinted summer ending,
Too late even for the crackling autumn's dying sigh,
The January Child
Dies, as he lived; in a strange land;
And in strange arms.
Dies in the grey dawning of a new youth,
And the grey twilight of a passing age.
Little wonder that in the birth of spring
We let our own darknesses lie forgotten.

Rachel Naylor (15)
(Highly commended)
1984

Jeremy, where's your father?

Jeremy, where's your father?
Why must they ask me?
They only do it to annoy
and because they know where he is
The teachers aren't much help either,
Write about a family outing . . .
Write about your family tree
Or in maths
If your mother gives you £2.50
and your father gives you . . . oh, sorry Jeremy
Wish they'd shut up about their fathers.
Philip's is a bank manager
Jen's is a teacher at another school.
Pete hardly sees his.
He's away a lot
On business trips
Matthew's are divorced.
At least that's respectable.
Everyone knows where my father is.
Ten years.
I'll be twenty-two by the time he's out.
Wish they'd stop talking about it,
it's not as if it's my fault.
Nobody seems to see I don't find it funny
when they laugh and smile secretly at each other
and ask me
Where's your father, Jeremy?

Sarah Todd (16)
Penparcau, Aberystwyth,
Dyfed
1990

'Under Pressure'
Philip Bentley (14)
1987

1984

I'm unapproved, unbeknown
Uncared for, uncredited
Undecided, uneducated
Unequal, unessential
Unfamed, unfashionable
Unfortunate, unfunded
Unhappy, unhoused
Unimportant, unloved
Unknowable, unmerited
Unnoticed, unpractical
Unrefined, unremembered
Unsatisfactory, unsheltered
Unsophisticated, untaught
Untrained, unversed
UNEMPLOYED!!

Alison Fell (14)
Filey, N. Yorks
1985

193

Asthma attack

The ground rushed towards me,
With a high-pitched scream.
Like a steam train,
Screeching at a sudden halt.

My chest heaved uncontrollably,
Sweat blurred my eyes,
Everything . . . turned a misty-grey.
I gasped for air,
Like a stricken
                man
                    gulping
                        water.

I rasped a feeble 'Help!'
It sounded like a broken, hoarse croak,
I was wet with sweat,
And exhaustion – rolling
                        as if in a
                            wrestler's
                                ring.

I clutched my chest,
Trying to rip out the pain,
That was tormenting my lungs.
A black cloud tore at my chest,
Trying to escape.
I was crying now,
Hot, stinging tears,
Poured ceaselessly,
Meandering down.
My wheezing,
A feverish energy,

Took hold of me,
As I pulled at the razor blade
Piercing my throat.
A black hole
      in my mind
           sucked
              me
                 in.

I was dimly aware of the nozzle,
Thrust into my mouth,
I inhaled the medicine, slowly,
      coughing,
      choking.
My eyes cleared.
I saw the worried face of a matron,
Peering at my white face.
The sweat still came,
I felt drained of energy – but
Propped myself on my elbow,
               smile!
          little
        a
      managed
   I even

William Somerville (12)
Tockington Manor School,
Tockington, Avon
1991

'Wardrobe'
Charlotte Howard (14)
1987

Elderly man

When she died
I didn't do the figures,
For I haven't the head
For such things.
They sent red letters through the door,
Demanding their money,
Always wanting more.
But I was so confused.

And in the end angry men
Came, took away my things
And then,
They came and took me.
'Didn't the neighbours ever pop in?
All on your own,
You poor old thing!'
They made it alright.
'There's quite a nice place
Near to here.
Why the sulky face?'
I was stupid to them,
Just another case,
An elderly man
To feed, to place.
Tuck me away.
My house, my kids, my Beth,
Held us in Life
But not so now in Death.
It's no longer mine.
They never found the key.
It was all changed
When I went back to see,
I died inside.

Helen Goff (14)
Uxbridge, Middx
1988

Remember me?

Remember me? I was your daughter,
The one you gave birth to
All those years ago.
Your hair was golden
And your eyes blue then,
Remember?

Remember me? I was your wife,
You used to drive me to the country
And we'd walk for miles . . .
And you'd take me on long weekends,
And cuddle me when I was cold.
Remember?

Remember me? I was your mother,
I used to powder you and change
    your nappy,
And rock you to sleep –
And love you
Yes, I used to love you
All those years ago.
Remember?

Remember me? I'm the senile patient
In ward 204.
The one who screams at night
    for some visitors.
But no one comes,
The one who mopes for her past –
Who throws food at the
    walls
And hits nurses.
Remember?

Jacqueline Kain (14)
1984

What the wolf knows

I'll hide under the covers
and wait.
She should have a surprise.
The key is under the stone
like always.
She should be here.
She should have her bright red cloak on,
so I should know who she is.
Her beautiful golden hair will flow.
She will scream.
I will eat her until
only her bones are left.
I will throw them on the fire
until they burn to a cinder.
She won't cry.
I will eat her quicker than
a lion eats a mouse.
I can see it now.
Her blood flowing like a stream.
My nose will smell her flesh.
My eyes gleam until she has gone.
I sleep like a baby.
My shining mouth glows and drips.
I know her death.

Rowan Taylor (8)
Whalley CE County Primary School,
Whalley, Lancashire
(Silver Medal Award winner)
1991

Being black

I am black and you are white
You say I'm wrong and you are right
I'm just the same as you and you
I do the same I do, I do

To you I'm just a passer-by
And you still hate me, tell me why
I'm just the same as him and him
Every bone and every limb

Don't call me coloured it's not true
I am not green and I'm not blue
I'm just the same as them and them
I'm not a tiger or a wren

Let's not fight and let's be friends
Let's shake hands and make amends
I'm just the same as you and you
I do the same I do, I do

Rachel Gillies (11)
Nether Robertland Primary School,
Stewarton, Ayrshire
1989

Harvest poem

Fruit and nuts and berries,
Growing ripe and sweet,
Vegetables and golden corn
All for us to eat.

Rich food in its plenty,
Picked and stored away,
While others in their countries
Are starving every day.

Mothers in the market,
Choosing what to eat,
Perhaps a rich fruit pudding
For a special treat.

In heats of Ethiopia,
Little grows on land.
A mother looks at the food for the day
Which only fills one hand.

In lands of drought and hunger
No more, dear Lord, we pray
Will mothers ask the question
Which child to feed today?

James Anthony Carey (10)
Guiseley, Leeds
1987

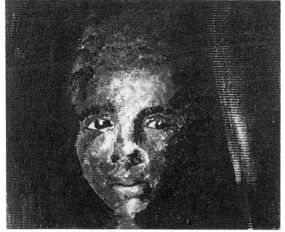

'Portrait of a Papua
New Guinean'
Gemma Lyus (13)
Honiton, Devon
1991

201

A mouse lived in a laboratory

The scientists dyed a mouse bright blue
To see what all its friends would do.
Its friends, they didn't seem to mind . . .
The scientists wrote down their find.

The scientists cut the mouse's brain
To see if it would act the same.
The mouse was still able to think . . .
The scientists wrote this down, in ink.

The scientists took the mouse's brain
Clumsily sewed it up again.
The mouse, it acted like a clown . . .
The scientists wrote all this down.

The scientists tied the mouse's feet
And buried it in soil and peat
The mouse quite liked it in the muck . . .
The scientists wrote this in their book.

Soon afterwards the scientists tried
To spin the mouse until it died.
The mouse loved whirring round and round . . .
(The scientists' pad was spiral bound.)

The mouse, by now immune to pain
Could not have been of use again.
Red cross through notes, and 'Mouse no good' . . .
The scientists wrote this down.
In blood.

Kathryn Boydell (15)
Heaton Norris, Stockport,
Cheshire
1988

The hedgehog

At dead of dayfall the spiky rustler comes.
Stout and fussy, the pincushiony foodnapper
Darkles down ditches,
Grubbling gardenwards.
A midnight rifler through black bin bags,
The scurrying spinysnorter sniffles and scuffles,
Snailsearching.

Then, gutfully, he porkles back
Across the slugslimed street,
Till, fearstruck by a blinding roar,
He bristleballs.
And is splattened.

Why did the pricklepig cross the road?

Sara-Louise Holland (11)
Whittlesford, Cambs.
(Highly commended)
1987

Blood sport

I chased the red confusion with my eye,
It scuttled fast, hungry eyed, across maps
Of snow. Birds rose like arrows in the sky
As it ran into thick, wet woods. Perhaps

They caught it, I don't know, I didn't stay
To watch the waves of galloping horses,
Their riders, lean and elegant, on their way
To find their fun. I only heard voices,

And they were not the shouts of red faced men.
That fortuitous sight smeared me like blood,
I kept thinking of the flexing fox, then
The chase, the bloody kill. I wished I could

Make sense of it all, feeling like I was
The hounded one, running wildly in snow;

It's 'sport', a 'show', no necessary cause –
They lost the true scent a long time ago.

Christopher Jones (16)
Quorn, Leicestershire
(Highly commended)
1986

'Halt at the Jump'
Rosanne Edwards (10)
1985

The snow-goose

A flutter in the reeds
As the flood tastes the marshes,
And from the sharp-edged grass,
Frost-frozen in the night, the snow-goose flaps.

The hoarfrost cracks, and is swallowed
In sponges of muddy moss,
As a flurry of soft feathers
Sink into the tide-soaked tufts.

A low whistle behind the brakes
And the eager panting of spaniel;
The snow-goose rises jerkily
In a sleep-stained panic of movement.

He spirals upwards, and hears
The silent click of a trigger.
Then a long cry as he plummets
Wildly like a melted corkscrew.

Catherine Skinner (16)
Hitchin, Herts.
(Highly commended)
1985

At the Table We Meet

Parents

At the table we meet.
I am somewhere between the two.
Where, what dreams do I fulfil,
How much of an extension?
I, the silent spectator,
Watching the sorrow on their chiselled features,
Watching each guise, lovers, parents, providers . . .
In proportion to age.
Have I replaced their bed
Their duty done, product centred?
The roles for me emerge
Darker and darker by every day.
Will I be ambushed before I'm thirty,
As I have ambushed them?

Iain McKenzie (16)
1984

Baby breakfast

Squidge
My food in my fist
Throw
It at the wall
Rub
It in my hair
Soak
It in my milk
Squeeze
The dirt out
Stuff
It in my mouth
Splurt
It across the room
Dig
It out of my bib
Catapult
It to Mummy
Aim
It at Daddy
Mmmm
Finished.

Julia Marsden (15)
1984

'Swimming'
Katherine Gilson (7)
1987

211

Newspaper

At breakfast time,
Mother, me and newspaper,
sit at the table,
I often wonder,
What's behind it;
Last time I looked,
it was my dad,
but I don't know if it still is.
We slowly plough through
our scrambled eggs,
in silence.
But the silence is sometimes broken,
by the rustle
of pages turning in front of my face.
I see the headlines
flash by,
'Nurses demand pay rise!'
'Is Lawson the Ladies' man?'
What can be
so entrancing
about a newspaper,
I ask myself.
Sometimes I hear
the odd grunt or comment,
coming from behind
the mysterious pages.
Very rarely,
I see a hand grab
at a cup of tea,
take it behind
the black and white pages,
and put it back.

Now hurry, son, dinna dander.
Nae playin' wi' yer mate.
Come on now, son, watch oot
Or ye'll be too late.
'Sorry, son, nae haggis.'
That's what the chipper wifie said.
What will a say tae mah dad?
He'll put me to mah bed!

Ah suppose a'd better tak' a keek,
Through a windae at a telly.
There's a big puddle here
I'll splash in it wi' mah wellies.
So what if a git a row,
I'll be awa' tae scule.
A micht ride mah cartie i' the morn,
Or bunk aff an' play the fool.

Stephen West (11)
Longhaugh Primary School,
Dundee
(Highly commended)
1989

Mealtimes

We love to eat at Nana's,
Because the food's so good.
There's lamb and ham and turkey
And beef with Yorkshire pud.
But better than the best of these
We like the cabaret,
Which Grandad always does for us,
And it makes Nana say
'Alec, peel the veg,
Don't let the custard burn.
Answer the door and where's my shoes,
Take off that shirt it's torn.
Peel the sprouts and where's my bag,
That gravy's much too thick.
Mop the floor, don't make a mess
and Alec do be quick.
Hoover the floor and feed the cat,
And make the strawberry flan.
There's just one thing I can't abide,
And that's a lazy man.'
And when at last poor Grandad comes,
To sit down at the table.
Nana gets him up again
As fast as she is able.
To make herself a cup of tea,
That's hotter than the last.
And woe betide you, Grandad,
If she doesn't get it fast!

Janey Mitson (9)
1984

A Shetland prayer

Thankdee lorde fur da sun an raen dat maks da
tatties, neeps an a da veegetebles dat grow.
An keeps wis lifen. An da fish wir faders cetch an
da ots da crofters grow fur da oneemals
dat gees wis milk on mit a thankdee lorde
fur da plants dat maks wir yeards a bonny.

This is Shetland dialect. Here is the translation:

Thank you Lord for the sun and rain
that makes the potatoes, turnips and
all the vegetables that grow
and keeps us living.
And the fish our fathers catch
and the oats the crofters grow for
the animals
that give us milk and meat.
I thank you Lord for the plants
That make our gardens beautiful.

Janine Riley (9)
Hamnavoe School,
Burra Isle, Shetland
1988

My parents argue

By the window
I watch some children on the lawn.
Press my cheeks against the cold glass.
See tears run down it.
Listen;
Screaming behind the door.
They slam each other's heads against the
wall with insults.
Tear hopelessly at the hair-fine thread
which attaches them both.
By the window
I smear the wet glass with my finger.
And distorted through it
I watch some children on the lawn.

Karen Heath (17)
Epsom, Surrey
1991

Third time lucky

I am now adopted for the third time;
Third time lucky they always say.
Maybe this adoption will bring me luck –
For my first adoptive parents I was too lazy.
For my second adoptive parents I was too fat.
For my third parents I might be just right.

I stand alone in my room staring at the ceiling,
I look around, everything seems just right.
The room looks expensive
The parents can't really be rich
If they were I definitely wouldn't be here.

My so-called parents keep staring at me;
Maybe they're wondering
'What have we adopted?'
My new mother says
'Don't touch the iron, it's hot.'
I know, I am fourteen, I say to myself.

My new father says
'Don't talk to strangers.'
I say to myself
I am already talking to strangers.

Pavandeep Lochab (13)
Cranford Community School,
Cranford, Middx
1988

I remember

'I remember,' she says,
'When I was a kid,
there were no worries,
we could go on the Ferry
to Liverpool and back,
or stay out till ten,
and my mum wouldn't worry,
down by the docks,
coming back from school,
we would talk to the sailors and fishermen.'

'As I remember it, this place that is,
wasn't an estate,
but all woods and fields,
we would come here for picnics,
and on Sundays, me, my mum, dad and Tom,
would all go to the beach,
we could leave the front door open, of course,
as I remember,' she says,
'but now you can't leave any door open,
or talk to people you don't know,
can't stay out till 8 o'clock,
even mum stays in,
dad doesn't like to be out either, after dark,
as I remember it,
we could stay out without going home, them days,
can't now.'

Mum says, 'Come straight home, love,
don't be late, you know how I worry.'
Those were the days, she says,
as I remember it,
she says,
as I remember it.

Rachel Girven (11)
Manor Junior School,
Birkenhead, Merseyside
(Highly commended)
1988

'Football Fans'
Nigel Brooke (14)
Salesian School,
Longhope, Gloucestershire
1991

Moving north with a daughter

You will not remember the thickness of trees
Or the quiet roads on our crowd of hills;
Sussex swelling her rivers and blowing cold.

Yorkshire slopes gentle and plunges deep;
It is all one to you on the garden rug,
The kiss of heather here, and the great spaces.

I remember villages spoiling for ground,
Rocks in the primal floor of the wood;
And I hear the small wicked sounds of your chuckle
Bubbling up, and bursting like bubbles.

Louise Bagshawe (17)
Woldingham School, Nr Caterham,
Surrey
(Italian Tour Award winner)
1989

Mechanics

My father worked above me, a spanner in his hand.
In the lemon sunlight he was a shadow against the blue
  sky;
A delicate blue, almost watery in the heat.
Beyond him yawned a sleepy field of green and yellow;
Cowslips nestled in the long grass like drops of honey.

But I became oblivious to the call of the summer
  landscape.
The gravel clawed at my bare legs as I sat beneath my
  father,
He dripped oil on my naked hot hands
And ruffled my hair with grimy, thick fingers.

The sun curved down to the hazy horizon
And the odour of searing rubber and sweating grease
Mingled with the soft flowery fragrance of evening.
A breeze delivered each smell to probe my nostrils
And my father rubbed my hands clean with a filthy rag.

Diane Susan Burgess (15)
(Highly commended)
1983

'Boat Builders'
Lupin Rahman (13)
Nonsuch High School for Girls, Cheam, Surrey
1989

223

The incredible bouncing man

Bouncing in and out of
Death's reach, as if he were on elastic:

My Grandad.

'Stand by your beds! Here comes Grandad!'
A permanent smile engraved on his face,
Walking stick in one hand, pint glass in the other.

But annually, at Christmas time, he goes that little bit
Too far, enjoys himself just too much,
Drains his seemingly eternal energy source,
And always ends in hospital.
The family sit round his bed.

Drips sustain his energy and blood level.
His eyes are closed.
The nurses have given up.
Tears form.
Grandad is a deathly white, mouth open, just breathing.
But by the end of that week he is always better.
Four heart attacks, three years of nearly dying at
    Christmas.
Two weeks to live in 1960, and twenty years of chain
    smoking:
He would never give in to septicaemia.

He's always back, drinking, eating and most of all
    talking,
With eighty-two years behind him and countless years in
    front,
Causing scandals in his old people's home,
Asking if widows can come and stay with him.

My Grandad is unique.
                    And wonderful.

Andrew M. Holgate Darley (13)
The King's School,
Canterbury, Kent
(Highly commended)
1986

'Swimmers'
Andrew Hunt (11)
Sir Hugh Owen Lower School
Caernarfon, Gwynedd
1990

My scream

From far away,
Down the sterile corridor,
A tiny cry comes.
A small murmur,
A whimper,
Develops a scream.
They are down there,
Smiling at the scream
Lovingly letting it fill them,
No thought of me.
I slide off my seat,
The sound of the scream
Still echoing through the silence.
My silence.
Slowly, I move,
Making my way
Amongst the mute hustle
That surrounds me.
Stretched, to my full short height,
I stare through the door
At the staring faces.
All eyes are focused
On the scream.
Slowly, my eyes lower towards it,
A small crinkled bundle,
Saturated in my mother's love.

Denise Daniels (15)
Ramsey Abbey School,
Ramsey, Cambridgeshire
1990

Momentary

Pale pink smile twitches to a halt,
Top lip sits tight and ominously on the protruding
   bottom one,
Tiny countenance angers,
Wrath feeds colour to its face
turning it into a quivering strawberry.
Eyes, damp blue, peer over mounds of compressed cheek,
Send forth hot tears that slide down the contorting nose
and are caught by a fat exploring tongue
Then whipped and concealed in its mouth,
The salty taste is examined.
   Suddenly, two pale eyes rise in wonder
over the subsiding cheeks.
A rich secure chuckle rises from his toes
causing the tight creased nose to unfold.
Red anger drains away like flood water.
The little body relaxes
And it sinks to sleep,
In a secure mass of white crocheted blanket
Like a little crumpled peach skin.

Lisa Robinson (13)
(Award winner)
1984

My brother Barry

He thinks he's a cool dude
In his winklepicker boots
And black leather coat.
His dark spiked hair
Makes him look like a hedgehog,
Red spots spangle
His chubby cheeks,
Everyone knows him better by
Monto.
He has a tough walk,
And an awkward run,
Always has three girlfriends
Not one.
You'd hear his car
In Timbucktoo
When he starts it in the morning,
He's no Elvis,
But to me, he's a star.

Glenn Montgomery (10)
St Mary's Primary School, Killyleagh,
Co. Down, N. Ireland
1989

'The Safari Park'
Kirsteen Ann Harvey (4)
1988

At the End

What's in a poem?

'What's in a poem?'
My brother asked one day   ?
'Although it isn't difficult
'I don't know what to say.'

'Oh! It's just imagination
'With a bit of inspiration,   !
'And a little application
It's a rhyme and time sensation!'

Nana Francois (9)
Summertown
Oxford
1990

Index of titles

232

Index of authors

Other great reads ⟍ *from* **Red Fox**

Further Red Fox titles that you might enjoy reading are listed on the following pages. They are available in bookshops or they can be ordered directly from us.

If you would like to order books, please send this form and the money due to:

ARROW BOOKS, BOOKSERVICE BY POST, PO BOX 29, DOUGLAS, ISLE OF MAN, BRITISH ISLES. Please enclose a cheque or postal order made out to Arrow Books Ltd for the amount due, plus 30p per book for postage and packing to a maximum of £3.00, both for orders within the UK. For customers outside the UK, please allow 35p per book.

NAME _____

ADDRESS _____

_____

Please print clearly.

Whilst every effort is made to keep prices low, it is sometimes necessary to increase cover prices at short notice. If you are ordering books by post, to save delay it is advisable to phone to confirm the correct price. The number to ring is THE SALES DEPARTMENT 071 (if outside London) 973 9700.

Other great reads from **Red Fox**

Discover the Red Fox poetry collections

CADBURY'S NINTH BOOK OF CHILDREN'S
POETRY
Poems by children aged 4–16.
ISBN 0 09 983450 2   £4.99

THE COMPLETE SCHOOL VERSE
ed. Jennifer Curry
Two books in one all about school.
ISBN 0 09 991790 4   £2.99

MY NAME, MY POEM ed. Jennifer Curry
Find *your* name in this book.
ISBN 0 09 948030 1   £1.95

MONSTROSITIES Charles Fuge
Grim, gruesome poems about monsters.
ISBN 0 09 967330 4   £3.50

LOVE SHOUTS AND WHISPERS Vernon Scannell
Read about all sorts of love in this book.
ISBN 0 09 973950 X   £2.99

CATERPILLAR STEW Gavin Ewart
A collection describing all sorts of unusual animals.
ISBN 0 09 967280 4   £2.50

HYSTERICALLY HISTORICAL Gordon Snell and
Wendy Shea
Madcap rhymes from olden times
ISBN 0 09 972160 0   £2.99

Other great reads *from* **Red Fox**

The latest and funniest joke books are from Red Fox!

THE OZONE FRIENDLY JOKE BOOK
Kim Harris, Chris Langham, Robert Lee,
Richard Turner

What's green and highly dangerous?
How do you start a row between conservationists?
What's green and can't be rubbed out?

Green jokes for green people (non-greens will be pea-green when they see how hard you're laughing), bags and bags of them (biodegradable of course).

All the jokes in this book are printed on environmentally friendly paper and every copy you buy will help GREENPEACE save our planet.

* David Bellamy with a machine gun.
* Pour oil on troubled waters.
* The Indelible hulk.

ISBN 0 09 973190 8   £1.99

THE HAUNTED HOUSE JOKE BOOK
John Hegarty

There are skeletons in the scullery . . .
Beasties in the bath . . .
There are spooks in the sitting room
And jokes to make you laugh . . .

Search your home and see if we are right. Then come back, sit down and shudder to the hauntingly funny and eerily rib-rattling jokes in this book.

ISBN 0 09 9621509   £1.99